Poems From Yorkshire

Edited by Steve Twelvetree

First published in Great Britain in 2005 by:
Young Writers
Remus House
Coltsfoot Drive
Peterborough
PE2 9JX
Telephone: 01733 890066
Website: www.youngwriters.co.uk

SB ISBN 1 84460 662 7

Foreword

Young Writers was established in 1991 and has been passionately devoted to the promotion of reading and writing in children and young adults ever since. The quest continues today. Young Writers remains as committed to engendering the fostering of burgeoning poetic and literary talent as ever.

This year's Young Writers competition has proven as vibrant and dynamic as ever and we are delighted to present a showcase of the best poetry from across the UK. Each poem has been carefully selected from a wealth of *Once Upon A Rhyme* entries before ultimately being published in this, our twelfth primary school poetry series.

Once again, we have been supremely impressed by the overall high quality of the entries we have received. The imagination, energy and creativity which has gone into each young writer's entry made choosing the best poems a challenging and often difficult but ultimately hugely rewarding task - the general high standard of the work submitted amply vindicating this opportunity to bring their poetry to a larger appreciative audience.

We sincerely hope you are pleased with our final selection and that you will enjoy *Once Upon A Rhyme Poems From Yorkshire* for many years to come.

Contents

Sacred Heart Primary School

Wellhouse J&I School

The Poems

Summertime

Summertime is here again,
Hip, hip, hip hooray,
I'm going to the beach,
To have a well cool day.
We're lying on the sand,
It's a wonderful day.
And a dog came up,
'Cause he wanted to play.
I've just got stung,
And it's by a bee.
It stung my arm,
And it really hurt me.
We're swimming in the sea,
And playing with a dog,
Mum keeps saying,
There's no such thing as fog.
Summer's nearly over,
So we're driving in our car.
We said goodbye to the beach
But we didn't get that far.

Rhiannon Spencer (11)
Athelstan Primary School

All Colours Autumn

The leaves are all crispy,
And the wind is all wispy.
As the leaves give a crunch,
The kids get a hunch.
They get on the winter coats,
There will be no more oats.
People wearing winter clothes,
And socks to cover toes!

Rebecca Romans (10)
Athelstan Primary School

The Door

(Inspired by 'The Door' by Miroslav Holub)

The door crept open,
The girl stepped in,
All she could see was
An old bin,
She opened it
Out came -
Spiders,
Scorpions,
Beetles,
Skeletons,
Zombies,
Vampires,
Monsters,
Then she saw
A haunted house,
She stepped in
And saw
A ghost
Not any old ghost
A mean ghost
She thought
Everything but nothing.

Martha Fletcher (8)
Athelstan Primary School

Seasons

Summer, spring, autumn, winter
There are all types of seasons
We have fun in all of them
Playing in the sun and snow
Summer, spring, autumn, winter.

Adam Fensom (9)
Athelstan Primary School

The Door

(Inspired by 'The Door' by Miroslav Holub)

The door creaked open
Kate stepped in
All she could see was darkness.

She saw an old box,
She stumbled over to it,
She opened the lid
She looked around.

She saw . . .
A garden, butterflies
A fluffy rabbit, colourful butterfly.

Kate's foreboding turned to happiness
She went to the swing
And stroked the rabbit.

Suddenly she felt tired
She lay down on the soft grass
Her eyes closed.

Chloe Ferguson (8)
Athelstan Primary School

The Door

(Inspired by 'The Door' by Miroslav Holub)

Go and open the door,
What will be behind it? I don't know.
There could be a mummy from Egypt,
Aliens or evil dogs.

Go and open the door,
What will be behind it? I don't know.
There could be a mummy from Egypt,
Aliens or evil dogs.

I'll just have a peek
Arghhh? A mummy!

Ashleigh Ivens-Green (8)
Athelstan Primary School

The Door

(Inspired by 'The Door' by Miroslav Holub)

I dare you
To open
The door
What's behind the door,
We do not know
There could be
A mummy from Egypt.

A dare you
To open
The door
There could be
A dog pound perhaps.

What's
Behind
The
Door?

Beth Beck (8)
Athelstan Primary School

The Door

(Inspired by 'The Door' by Miroslav Holub)

'Open the door little boy'
But what could be behind there?
A scarab beetle?
An enormous hive of wasps?

'Open the door little boy'
But what could be behind there?
A ghost?
Or a humungous dinosaur?
But at last he opened the door
And then he saw it but it was another dimension.

James Cole (9)
Athelstan Primary School

The Door

(Inspired by 'The Door' by Miroslav Holub)

Open the door
You'll never know what's out there,
There might be a mummy in the dump ground
With blood dripping out of its mouth.

Open the door there might be
Some treasure waiting to be found
With thousands of money and jewels.

Please go open the door
There might be a unicorn
Waiting to be rode.

Open the door,
Open the door!
There might be a princess.

I dare you to open the door
Scaredy-cat, ha, ha, ha, ha!

Faye Jacques (8)
Athelstan Primary School

The Door

(Inspired by 'The Door' by Miroslav Holub)

'Open the door!' 'Open the door!'
What is it? Is it a black dog bouncing?
A white ghost flying round
Or mum making a cup of tea?
'Go on, open the door'
There might be chocolate -
Or ice cream
Or a fire-breathing dragon.
'Open the door!'
There could be a blood-sucking vampire
Or a zombie
Or a dinosaur in the dark.

Joe Wilson (8)
Athelstan Primary School

The Door

(Inspired by 'The Door' by Mirsolav Holub)

It's all a terrible dream, it must be!
Said the small voice inside her
Suddenly an eerie sound
Came from the door
It must be a big dog.

Don't open the door
Whatever you do.
It could be an ear-splitting scream
Or it could be a mythical dragon or a ghost
Maybe a scary witch on a broomstick.

Cr maybe a dazzling princess in a pure gold dress
Perhaps a naughty, sprightly goblin
Or a dark damp nothing.

Katie Hayes (8)
Athelstan Primary School

The Door

(Inspired by 'The Door' by Miroslav Holub)

Go open the door, the creepy door
See what's behind the creepy door
A zombie? A vampire? A ghost?
Go open the creepy door
See what's behind the creepy door
A doomy doom? An alive skeleton? Some bats?
Go see what's behind the creepy door.

Go open the creepy door
There might be a giant who lives in a dark alley?
Or a magic hat who lives in a haunted castle?
Or some spiders that live in a box?
Go open the door the creepy door
At least there will be a draught.

Jessica Hull (8)
Athelstan Primary School

The Door

(Inspired by 'The Door' by Miroslav Holub)

Walk down the dark dripping alleyway little boy!
He took a step forward
He started to see a door.
He stared at it for a while,
Then he started to run to it
Stop! Said a voice in his head.

What's behind the crooked door?
Is it light?
Is it darkness?
Even if it's just a wall, just open it!
'No!' he replied shivering
The little boy walked in complete silence.
Silently the door creaked open
The little boy started to run
Suddenly he woke up
His heart was in suspense
What's behind the door? Is it . . .?

Jack Skinner (8)
Athelstan Primary School

Autumn Days

Autumn days when you have some fun
And the leaves fall off the trees in the sun.

We play all day and sometimes night
And as I go home there's a lovely sight.

I play in the leaves all crispy and crackly
And then watch the fireworks go *boom!*

The days are getting shorter, the nights are drawing in.
The air getting much colder because autumn has come again.

Callum Miller (9)
Athelstan Primary School

The Door

(Inspired by 'The Door' by Miroslav Holub)

Walk down the alleyway little girl
Who knows what's at the end?
An owl hooted and rats ran past her feet.
She stepped forward into the darkness
She was everywhere
But nowhere.
Rain ran down her spine.
Her life was in suspense.
She knew nothing
She saw a door.
She walked over to it,
Put her hand on the handle.
What was behind it?
She could only wander
She pulled the handle
Suddenly she woke up.
It was only a dream
What could happen in the real thing?

Joe Marner (8)
Athelstan Primary School

Summer

S un shines all day and night
U nder the trees
M idday it's hot
M ilkshakes are being drunk
E arly in the morning the sun dawns
R eady to lay in the sun.

Meghan Tattersall (9)
Athelstan Primary School

Hurricane Francis

One cold and wet September day
Hurricane Francis hit Tampa Bay
She blew down trees and knocked off slates,
She even blew down garden gates.

The roads ran like rivers, it gave us the shivers
Everyone stocked up their fridges,
As the police close all the bridges.

The sea started to swell what a tale to tell
The wind was so strong,
It pounded like the beat of the gong,
No shops were taking any chances with Francis.

48 hours of total madness
Come the morn just a tropical storm

Wave goodbye to Hurricane Francis
As she makes her way to Tallahassee.

Danielle Holroyd (10)
Athelstan Primary School

Winter Days

W hen the lights are up
I nside and out
N o shops are open
T rees in the houses that smell like pine
E njoyable snow falling from the sky
R ain with snow.

D oors are locked
A ll kids excited
Y es it's Christmas
S anta is here.

Jamie Fletton (10)
Athelstan Primary School

Winter

Winter days when the grass is covered
And we're all inside our cosy homes.
When we're sat down with the fire burning
And we're on our mobile phones.

It's a winter day
It's a cold winter day
It's always so freezing
It's a winter day.

All the time we are wrapped up in our mittens
And playing snowball fights all day.
Thinking about Jesus being born in a stable
But that's just what they say.

It's a winter day
It's a cold winter day
It's always so freezing
It's a winter day.

William Haigh (9)
Athelstan Primary School

Wind Whispering Winter

Dark nights in wind whispering winter.
Fluffy white polar bears hunting for strong smelling fish.
Penguins also hunting in gruesome green, salty seas
For ice-blue, slippery, scaly fish.
While baby crisp white seals flapper up and down the ice.
Icicles are clashing and smashing as the wind swiftly blows
This is what it is like in wind whispering winter.

Emma Barker (10)
Athelstan Primary School

Summer

Summer is the world's best season because,
There is ice cream,
All the snow has gone,
And now we know
That summer is here.

People going on holiday,
Having a good time,
See the bright yellow sun,
Everyone shouts because summer is here.

Now summer comes to an end,
All the nights get longer,
People grow sad,
Because summer has gone.

Ryan Addey (10)
Athelstan Primary School

The Autumn Poem

Autumn days when the leaves are free
And the sounds of the autumn!
Leaves go *crackle, crackle, crackle.*

Every Friday I go out and play
And step on all of the brown leaves
They're going *crunch, crunch, crunch.*

I look out of my window and
See all of the leaves falling from the sky.

I like going out on Fridays
And seeing all the leaves
Turning brown and crispy.

Shannon Chappell (9)
Athelstan Primary School

The Rabbit In The Warren

My rabbit is as pure as snow
Her eyes are so bright you'd say they glow,
Her face is fluffy, furry and white
As she runs from the wolf with all her might.

She is cuddly and cute
In her furry white suit
She is fluffy and smart
And she runs like a dart.

In her home underground
There is always something to be found
She stays in her hole all day
Never comes out to play.

Neelam Riaz (10)
Boothroyd J&I School

The Robin

Swooping sliding in the sky
The robin flies his wings up so high
The sun is dazzling, hot and bright
What a great, beautiful light.

The robin's breast sparkling like a jewel.
The breezy wind blows, it's so cool.
The trees sway left to right.
The robin's flight is a pretty sight.

The robin sings a chirpy song
He sings and sings all day long
I love to listen to him sing,
As I watch him flap his wings.

Anisa Jamil (11)
Boothroyd J&I School

Tiger

Tiger! Tiger! Tall in height
When it gives us a big fright,
Day or night we shiver holding on tight to our friends
The tiger then does his trends.

Walks past trees, through the forest with nothing better to do
It never opens its door even if you say it's you
Tigers - extremely old
And also very bold.

Tiger's colours fading away
Tiger is very gay
It lays inside feeling tired
Tiger is like he's been fired.

Tiger is off to die
Tiger's temperature goes high
We must save Tiger.

Harun Nawaz (10)
Boothroyd J&I School

My Dog

My dog is fluffy
More than my cat buffy
Its eyes are bright
It sleeps all night.

When my dog is bad
It makes my grandma mad
He chews up my socks
I hide them in a box.

He plays with his ball
No matter how small,
He chases my cat
She hides under the mat.

Shane Laraib (10)
Boothroyd J&I School

Hallowe'en

Can you guess what it's time for?
Goblins and witches and ghouls.
I hope you don't get too easily scared
It's not the time for fools.

Goblins with boils on their faces
Slavering big purple lips
They all have spiders in their dirty hair,
Teeth that are full of blood drips.

Watch out! Old witches flying high
Cackling echoes all around
With long black hair and big hairy cats
There is always a horrible sound.

Can you guess what it's time for?
Goblins and witches and ghouls
I hope you don't get too easily scared
It's not the time for fools.

Rachel Simpson (11)
Boothroyd J&I School

Ghosts!

I'm in my bedroom,
All alone with the light switched off.
And the door closed tightly
It looks like something coming closer and closer.
Is it ghosts? It better not be.
I'm feeling like I'm going to fall in tears
And noises coming from outside
I wanna go to sleep but I'm scared
My eyes are droopy and red so I'll say goodnight,
Until I go to sleep but watch out for the ghosts.

Nafeesah Jamil (10)
Boothroyd J&I School

Mummy

I was in a tomb when I heard a growl
I ran with fright
And there it was, I heard a howl,
It was very dark, in fact it was night.

I screamed and screamed
Then the tomb was falling apart.
That is what it seemed,
When the mummy approached I could see his heart.

I finally got out
And then I saw the mummy
He gave a loud shout
And then he disappeared, I could only see his tummy.

Kasim Aziz (11)
Boothroyd J&I School

The Scary Figure

It was a very frightening night
I saw a scary figure
There wasn't a speck of light
He had a gun, he pulled the trigger.

I had to run, this wasn't fun
I ran and ran and ran
He tried shooting me with his gun
He shot the back of a van.

The door swung open
I jumped inside the back
I could tell he wasn't joking
By the way he sprang the attack.

Asif Hussain (10)
Boothroyd J&I School

My Little Sister And The Teacher!

My little sister
    Is a little blister
She put a snail
    On top of the teacher's nail.

My sister's teacher got mad
    My little sister was sad
She didn't eat that night
    She never turned on the light.

She swore at the teacher
    And thought, *that will teach her*
The teacher screamed!
    And she just beamed!

'What shall I do!' the teacher moaned
    My little sister just groaned
I could lock you up in a shoe box
    Or lend you to a fox.

I am so brave
    I'll try to behave
Come to my street
    I'll give you a treat.

Nabila Akhtar (10)
Boothroyd J&I School

Football

F ootball is the best, no other sport can beat it.
O h yes, what a goal!
O ne half cheers, one half groans
T he fans cheer and drum because their team has scored.
B oot the ball in the back of the net.
A lan Smith has been sent off.
L a, la, la, the fans sing
L ighten up Old Trafford, United have won.

Amin Jahangir (10)
Boothroyd J&I School

My Fantasy Island

I live in a fantasy island
Where all my dreams come true
The sun is dazzling in the sky
The sky is sapphire blue.

All you can hear are mermaids singing
That makes you want to dance
The peaceful music flows in the air
And you just have to take a glance.

The sea is like a pale blue picture
The sun is like a golden ball
The sand is a soft, crumbly mixture
It's so quiet; I can hear the birds call.

There's lots more things about my island
But I can't tell you all on a letter
If you come to my island
You will understand much better.

Zeba Hussain (10)
Boothroyd J&I School

Monkey

The monkey stays in the jungle
Swinging from tree to tree all day long
Whenever you see him he's climbing trees,
Up trees and down trees.

Bananas in his belly about half a dozen,
If you're really quiet you'll hear them rumbling
And moving around in his belly.

He's never heard of telly, but you just watch it all the time.
They eat bananas whenever you see and whenever you see them
If he sees you he'll throw some bananas at your head,
You'll fall down and be half dead.

Raza Ali (10)
Boothroyd J&I School

Footprints

I was in bed asleep
Something came up the stairs
It woke me up
Who could it be?
Who could I see?

I felt fearsome
Something went downstairs
I followed the muddy footprints,
Something stinks!

It opened the fridge
To see what it could find
It found nothing
It just looked behind.

I went further and further
Down the stairs
The next thing I know
It was eating some pears.

It ambled into the living room
When it was comfortable
I heard a loud boom.

It knocked things over
And I turned the light on
It was my dog Rover 'Oh Rover.'

Samantha Littlewood (10)
Boothroyd J&I School

???????

I don't believe in magic
Well I didn't till yesterday
When I was walking through the woods
One dark and stormy day.

I heard the voice of a man
I saw a flash of light
I thought it could be a wizard
But it couldn't be right?

I decided to go nearer
I decided to find out more
I finally met a man
But what was he there for?

I asked him what he was doing
He said, 'You'll find out soon.'
The sky suddenly became darker
So the stars gleamed beside the moon.

There was an almighty bang
I jumped up, scared out of my skin
Wait, I was back in my room
Still not knowing anything!

Amber Gavin (10)
Boothroyd J&I School

The Mummy

'Boo! Quickly hide or else I'll get you
You will scream, I am coming for you
I'll be wrapping you up
Don't think I won't!'

'No, please don't
I'm not scared of you
I'll run and hide
You won't get me'.

'Crash, See I told you
I'll scrunch you like I did to the others
Gotcha!
Tickly under there?'
'Mum don't, it tickles me
Don't Mum! Please stop!'

'I just want to tickle you,
Sweetie, to make you happy
And to make you laugh'.

Shafeela Shawkat Alam (11)
Boothroyd J&I School

Furry Cat

The cat is as black as the night
He always tries to play in the light
He loves to fight
He always tries to get out of sight.

His eyes are as blue as the sky
He always tries to make me fly
He always tries to jump so high
He always gets my sock and I say *mine.*

He is as light as a mouse
Always tires to get in other's house
His ears are as floppy as silk
He loves to drink some milk.

Aneesha Rafiq (10)
Boothroyd J&I School

Dreams

I always want my dreams to come true,
But they never seem to.
I once dreamt that I was in paradise,
It was the best dream I ever had.

Delightful faces full with happiness.
People were full with enjoyment
It seemed like that it was the gift of pleasure
Gentle music flowing in the air.

Beautiful flowers, which have a charming smell,
Which drift you to sleep.
Everyone dancing and enjoying themselves.
Charming waterfalls flowing.

If only it came true!

Henna Sabir (10)
Boothroyd J&I School

Foxy Fox

Foxy fox licks the tins
When you find them in the bins
If you see them in the town
You'll be happy, you won't frown.

Foxy fox is brown and red
She sleeps all day in a cosy bed
At night she goes out for her lunch
And brings it home to munch! Munch! Munch!

Foxy fox with her baby cub
In the bath rub-a-dub-dub
With her bright red coat - a pretty girl
Long pointy ears, eyes bright as a pearl.

Shannon Barrowcliffe (10)
Boothroyd J&I School

Football - Manchester United

United are the champions
They always win their matches
They score a lot of goals
Given any chances.

They get possession of the ball
He takes it up the pitch
Giggs gets tripped to the ground
Penalty area, Smith scores.

United is winning 1-0
From the halfway line kick
What a fantastic goal
It's 2-0 to Man U.

It's a free kick to Manchester
Ronaldo is taking it
He shoots, oh hits the post!
Rooney scores the rebound
The whistle is blown for full-time.

Final score 3-0.

Zakir Momoniat (11)
Boothroyd J&I School

Dog, Cat And Mouse

Down the winding street
A cat ran after a mouse
A dog saw the cat
He chased the cat.

Down the winding street
The dog chased the cat
The cat ran after the mouse
The mouse came to a dead end.

Down the winding street
The mouse was crossing the road
Suddenly in came a car
Splat! The mouse was no more.

Down the winding street
The cat was getting tired
The dog was catching up
The cat could go no further.

Down the winding street
The cat collapsed to the ground
The dog caught up and ate the cat
Down the winding street.

Waqar Chaudhary (10)
Boothroyd J&I School

My Brother!

My brother is a big baboon
He always watches Loony Toons
He just eats and eats
And then gets a big beat.

He's got a big tummy
And then calls for his mummy
He is so cruel
He thinks he should rule.

My brother is a big, fat nut
And he always goes to a hut.
He thinks he's so cool
He never does his work at school.

He doesn't know his teacher's name
And he always plays a silly game.
Whilst he wears his tie
You always see him eating a pie.

Needa Patel (10)
Boothroyd J&I School

It's Hallowe'en

H allowe'en here, it's scary as can be!
A ll the witches and ghouls are coming out to play!
L ittle children trick or treating will they get a lot of sweeties?
L ots of little children waiting for more candy!
O h! Don't be shy come as you are!
W e are here on Hallowe'en night!
E veryone is trick or treating!
E veryone is screaming because all the ghosts are squealing!
N ow Hallowe'en is over so next year have more fear!

Shona Heaton (10)
Churchfield Primary School

The Attic Monster

T he monster of the attic
H e is always there
E ndless creepy noises

A t the bottom of the stairs
T he monster of the attic he never goes away
T hen he gets his cobwebs and tries to take you away
I t keeps attacking your bedroom
C an't it ever stop?

M oaning at your doorstep, he wants a drink of pop
O h no, where is he now?
N ot in the kitchen
S omewhere in the house
T earing up my bedroom
E ven on the couch.
R un away and if you're lucky you will get away.

Jake Buckingham (9)
Churchfield Primary School

Hallowe'en

H aunted houses
A re around us looking side to side
L ittle vampires creeping round the cemetery
L icking germs, bug's off our bedroom wall
O ctopuses sleeping under your bed
W itches flying round your house
E xactly how they planned too
E ating candy like brandy
N ow the witches, ghost, ghouls are gone, slowly.

Ashley Maw (9)
Churchfield Primary School

Here Is Hallowe'en

Here is Hallowe'en
No one has to be seen.

The ghosts are here
So lets be clear.

Be careful what you do
The ghosts are after you.

Getting loads of candy
Might be very handy.

Street lights are flickering
The ghosts are jiggling.

Dogs are barking
Neighbours shouting.

Hallowe'en is here
So let's be clear next year!

Megan Green (10)
Churchfield Primary School

Hallowe'en

H orrible and spooky creatures
A nd old, scary, spooky things,
L oud, horrible, scary monsters,
L oud, horrible, scary creatures,
O ld UFOs have come to stay,
W eird and wonderful slimy things,
E verything's spooky now,
E verything's super scary,
N ow it's a scary day.

Jake Hanson (9)
Churchfield Primary School

The Shadow

It was the night of Hallowe'en
I lay there in my bed,
I saw a shadow on my wall,
'Don't be silly' my mother said.

I went back up to my bedroom,
The shadow started to move,
It didn't look like a human,
My brain just couldn't sooth.

I froze all of a sudden,
I dare not leave my room,
My heart started to beat fast,
Then it started to *boom!*

I heard a strange noise,
It was coming from my hat,
I went to lift my hat up,
And found it was my cat.

Bethan Gagen (9)
Churchfield Primary School

Hallowe'en

Hallowe'en is coming,
All the ghosts are stunning
I was lying in my bed,
When I saw a shadow on my bed
My mother said, 'Don't be silly,'
I see it again on my door,
I hear booms and bangs
It made me shiver under my bed,
But all it was was my little brother dressed up.

Natasha Whincup (9)
Churchfield Primary School

Bonfire Night

B onfire Night when bangs are here
O n the day of witches is queer
N ot it's time for the flames to appear
F ireworks, bonfires all things loud
I like the scene and I hope I don't scream
R ain came to wet, us very mean
E verybody round me, as I watched the crowd appeared to look up.

N ight dies away as day appears
I snuggle up tight
G o to the fire, watch it crackle
H ey big blue moon coming out to get me
T o all I see is next year.

Emily Key (10)
Churchfield Primary School

Hallowe'en!

H aunted classrooms,
A nd haunted schools,
L aughing faces and fearsome ghouls,
L ightning striking everywhere
O range pumpkins here to scare
W itches watching, witches waiting,
E eek go the brooms as their ends are skating
E very day and every night the ghouls come to give a fright
N ever forget this fearsome night or you could get a fright.

Emily Murphy (10)
Churchfield Primary School

Bonfire Night

B onfire Night
O n 5th November
N ice 'n' loud
F or the crowd to remember
I shouted with amazement as
R ockets banged
E veryone smiled.

N ow the shouting ended
I n a flash and a boom
G angs of people clapped with joy
H ats flew up to the sky up ahead.
T hen everything ended when I was in my bed!

Savannah Gillow (10)
Churchfield Primary School

Hallowe'en

H ats black, cloaks black
A werewolf walking round my room
L ittle ghost going down my street.
L onely devil eating wheat.
O ur house full of ghosts and ghouls
W itches on their broomsticks in a spooky school.
E very time it freaks me out.
E ager to see a devil shout.
N ow Hallowe'en is here, tomorrow won't be spooky.

Ellie-Jo Clarkson (10)
Churchfield Primary School

Werewolves

W erewolves in the park
E very time it's dark
R ound the corner there's a man
E very tooth looks like a fang
W herever you look there's a shadow
O ver the park, over the street, everywhere you look
L urking around in the shadows you may meet a mysterious fellow
F lowing through the street, creeping through the shadows
    And through the town.
    Sneaking up behind you trying to take you down.

Adam Firth (9)
Churchfield Primary School

Hallowe'en

It's Hallowe'en
Everything's scary
They've got masks on that are hairy
Ghouls, ghosts, witches, zombies.
They're all here
Even a guy dressed up as a reindeer.

It's Hallowe'en
Everything's creepy
Frankenstein's here but he's sleepy
There's a ghost in the park
But it doesn't know the time 'cause it's 12 and dark.

Danny Norburn (10)
Churchfield Primary School

The Ghost Of Classroom 2

The ghost of classroom 2,
It comes round smelling of poo,
Before you know it, it's on the floor,
Creeping under the classroom door.

The ghost of classroom 2,
It comes out and scares you too,
When she's creeping under the classroom door,
She looks like a big flat boar.

The ghost of classroom 2,
It leaves a trail of goo,
Be careful you don't slip because it's saliva spit.

Luke Jones (10)
Churchfield Primary School

Hallowe'en

H airy, happy, horrible
A ngry, awful,
L ots of money,
L ots of scary people
O range pumpkins
W orried,
E xcited,
E njoyable,
N ight-time.

Todd Patton (10)
Churchfield Primary School

Hallowe'en Creepers

Hallowe'en is coming
See that all is stunning.

I see a shadow on my bed,
'Don't be silly,' my mother said.

I see that shadow on my bed
'Don't be silly,' my mother said.

All the ghosts make me shiver,
All you do is want to quiver.

I call my mum and all of a sudden
I see a ghost and it makes be boast.

All I hear is bangs and booms,
I turn around and there is the noise again.

I went downstairs to my mum
But the ghost had took my mum.

Rachel Manley (10)
Churchfield Primary School

Hallowe'en Night

Hallowe'en it's so scary
Werewolf masks that are hairy
Dracula coming to my door
Now I'm on the kitchen floor
Witches, ghouls in the streets.
Always asking for sugary treats.
I'm glad it's only on one night.
Or I would die of fright.

Jamie Norburn (10)
Churchfield Primary School

The Cosmic Monster

Spooky and freaky you know it's there
The cosmic monster is here to grab
A fool which could be you
Run away from the cosmic monster
Yes before you know it you'll be gone.

My fish have disappeared, it's the cosmic monster
On my shelf I can hear it rattling my drawers
No no! It can't be the
Spooky cosmic monster at
The bottom of my bed
Erk! The noise it made
Rattling my ragged belt it had me, I know it!

Joe Birkin (9)
Churchfield Primary School

Hallowe'en

H at's are on the window sill,
A pples red like blood.
L ittle devils in the street.
L onely ghosts float round the room
O ur house full of witches and goblins
W itches on their brooms
E veryone spooked out of their skins,
E ager to see a cat flying
N ow it's time to go to bed, it should be over soon.

Stevie Parkin (10)
Churchfield Primary School

The Rap Dog

The rap dog who lives in ma street!
He barks a rappin' rappin' beat!
He sings a song in tune!
Then dances with his feet!

He wears a dark leather jacket!
And shades on his face!
His jeans are ripped and ragged!
And he moves at an amazing pace!

He performs in front of top judges,
And gets the best marks!
Then goes home to celebrate,
And his family gives him three barks!

Sam Wade & Josh Waddell (10)
Crossley Street Primary School

The Witch

There is a witch
With a big green nose
She has flaming orange hair
And pointy black toes.

She's always giving
Little children a fright
And she always flies
On her broomstick at night.

She climbs on the roof
And steals little children's toys
But she has to be careful
Not to make too much noise.

Katie Gaunt (9)
Crossley Street Primary School

The Little Mouse's Life

I'm a little mouse
Eating cheddar cheese
I love it so much
Can I have some more please?

I like to run around
In my little wheel
Having fun all day
Makes me feel like an eel.

My owners are really loving
They like me so much
They play with me every day
And even gave me a hutch.

I'll always love my owners
Today and forever
They make life so easy
We'll always be together.

Savannah Skiggs & Charlotte Draper (9)
Crossley Street Primary School

The Silly Naughty Dog

The small black and white dog
That lives on queen's lane
Comes through the cat flap
And is a right pain!

It runs round and round the house
Chasing the tabby cat
It bites my sister's shoe
And lands flat on my red hat!

He digs in the washing basket
Leaves dirt on the floor
Rips the wallpaper
And scratches the blue door!

Lois Etheridge & Abbie Barlow (9)
Crossley Street Primary School

The Man Next Door

The man next door
Is very fat and chubby
And gives a great roar.

When he sees me in the garden
He scrapes his claws
At his patio door
Yes that's him
That's the man next door.

You won't want to get on his bad side
Never, not now
It's him I can't abide.

When he stomps his feet
It's like an earthquake
He's got black hair all over him
I'm warning you he is scary
He even chucked a kitten
In a smelly old bin.

So I'm warning you
You won't want to lie dead on the floor
So try not to meet him
Because he is the man next door.

Bethany Cairnes (9)
Crossley Street Primary School

Shark

The ultimate shark is so frightening
It's as quick as lightning.

It goes everywhere
It's here no it's there.

It comes to eat some fish
Brings them back to its dish.

Try catching him if you can
You can't do it young man.

His shiny teeth are going to get you soon
I would swim if I were you.

So come find the shark
This is sure to be a laugh.

The
Scary
Speedy
Smart
Silent
Manoeuvrable
Cunning
Invisible
Hidden
Shark!

Samuel Owen (9)
Crossley Street Primary School

Motorbike On The Move

The motorbike is so frightening
It whizzes like lightning.

It gets through dark
As quick as a spark.

But when it's wet
It's really quite a pet.

It swerves through like a winding snake
That is awake.

It drives so fast
That it will never last.

It has a horn that goes beep
And it will not let you sleep.

It sounds like a bell
From Hell.

Sam McKay & David Adair (9)
Crossley Street Primary School

The Galloping Pony

The galloping pony
Running forever,
If you say, 'When will you stop?'
He answers back, 'Never!'

Dancing and prancing
Running around,
Twirling and whirling
Never touching the ground.

Faye Ripley & Jenny Rafferty (9)
Crossley Street Primary School

The Ringwraith And The Nazgul

It lurks in the shadows of the dead city
Its Nazgul is a vicious creature.

The Ringwraith for certain
Searches for the one ring.

The Nazgul full of sound and death
Carries a powerful scream.

These dead creatures
Are made out of elves.

These dead kings wear
A black hooded cloak.

The Nazgul flies around
Searching for prey.

Until they get destroyed
By the one ring!

Ben Filler & Michael McNamara (9)
Crossley Street Primary School

The Owl

When you hear its
Blood-curdling call at night
And its sharp shiny claws
The ghost-like white owl swoops down
With its short pointed beak
And scoops up a terrified field mouse.

Ryan McCarlie (9) & Alex Blanchard (10)
Crossley Street Primary School

Dolphins

Dolphins having moving tails
Dolphins have pointy fins
Dolphins have cute faces
Dolphins have smiley grins.

Dolphins are mammals
But not fish
They flick their pointy
Tails and go *swish!*

Dolphins live in water
Dolphins like to play
Dolphins like to swim
They make friends all day . . .

. . . Dolphins are good!

Natalie Collier & Kasha Havis (9)
Crossley Street Primary School

Jaws 2

Sharp, big, white teeth, ready
To attack
Small bright eyes
Long fins swerving through
The sea.
Man-eating shark swimming in
Your pool.

Great white coming to you
Ripping you into pieces
Slivery slimy shark
Slivering through the sea
Smelling blood to get you.

Jordan Wright (9)
Crossley Street Primary School

Holidays

When we go on holiday,
We can't wait,
We wonder what language they will speak,
Then the plane hits the ground,
It goes bump!
And you know you are there.

You get to the hotel
And have a look around
You bounce on the bed
And you have lots of fun
That night you think . . .
What you will do the next day?
Wish you were here.

Raven Hebden (10)
Drighlington Primary School

What If?

What if there were rules?
What would happen?
What if they were all over the universe?
Would it be bad or good?
What if people ignored rules?
Would they fight or not?
What if they were my rules?
What would happen?
What if?

Jamie Broadhead (10)
Drighlington Primary School

Rivers

Fast, quiet, slow,
These are noises of the river
Sometimes calm, sometimes crashing, banging loudly.

The river runs through valleys calm and quietly.
The river goes through the city
Loudly and bangs against the sides.

Chelsea Firth-Beety (10)
Drighlington Primary School

Rules

We have rules for our safety
In school or in the pool.
I am asking these questions
For you and me
To bring peace and harmony
To the school and all around,
We thank the Lord for these rules
To keep us safe all day long.

Josh Johnson (10)
Drighlington Primary School

Rules

Rules, rules where can they be?
At home and school,
What type of rules?
Safety and care,
Rules are good because they make you safe,
We have rules so there is no danger.

Ben Moylan (10)
Drighlington Primary School

Rivers

When rivers flow fast,
They thrash and thrash,
Scraping the bank sides bare.
When rivers are calm,
They seem so peaceful.
Drifting layer after layer,
When rivers overflow,
They cause devastation,
As the citizens are completely unaware.

Faye Woodham (10)
Drighlington Primary School

Beach

Crabs crawl in the rocks,
Shellfish hide in the sand,
Dolphins screech in the waves.

We play in the sand
Running in and out of the sea.

Sand, sun
Buckets, spades
Sky, sea.

Katie Bentley (10)
Drighlington Primary School

Sport

Running to the halfway line,
Now's my time to shine,
He shoots it, dips it, curls it, goes up and down,
It goes up, it dips down, he scores
The players go wild, the players hug me,
And we win one nil.

Joshua Wade (10)
Drighlington Primary School

I Wish

I wish I could ride the world
I wish I could gallop
I wish I could trot
I wish I could jump the moon
I wish I could be in a race
I am the best pony in the world
My name is black beauty
And this is what I am going to do today
Trot, gallop! Trot, gallop!

Angelina O'Donovan (7)
Drighlington Primary School

Rules

Rules, where do we use rules?
At schools, work, even at home.
Everybody uses rules from the
Poorest and even to the richest.
Why do we need rules?
For safety and emergency
We all need rules even you and me.

James Felton (11)
Drighlington Primary School

Things Found In A Goblin's Sack

A mini motorbike with extra bullets and lasers.
A secret hole where no one can find it.
A pot of magic dust that makes you into your worst nightmare.

Jake Kidd (7)
Drighlington Primary School

A Special Horse

I had a special horse
That loved to watch 'Inspector Morse',
She did a pretty dance,
And a very posh prance.

Her name was Lear
She liked to trot to the pier,
We sang twiddledee,
In the sea
That was the end of Lear.

Hetty Sunderland (10)
Drighlington Primary School

The Storm

I sit inside listening to the storm,
Raindrops from dark candyfloss clouds,
The icy wind blows the leaves and branches to the ground,
The lightning flashes in the sky,
Thunder bangs and crashes loudly
Rain turns to hail and white hailstones fall to the ground
making a loud noise
Just then the sun comes out and a rainbow appears in the sky.

Ashleigh Henry (9)
Drighlington Primary School

Sunset Gardens

People can play in the garden
Surrounded by beautiful flowers
But as the grass grows
The wind sways in the breeze
And as the sunset begins to set over the garden
The trees start to fall asleep.

Samantha Ingle (9)
Drighlington Primary School

The Rocket

I was very proud
In this huge roaring crowd
To see my father walk away
Into a rocket I must say
Oh what a sight to see
Maybe he's been thinking about me
I'm only five
I hope he comes back alive
But I liked the fiery wave
Inside that gloomy smoke
The sight I could not face
My dad blasting off into space
Smaller and smaller he became
Soon I'd forgotten his name
The roaring crowds all died away
But now I knew he'd be back soon
My dad, the first man on the moon.

Alex Gray (10)
Drighlington Primary School

Street Children

We street children have nothing to spare
Only the clothes on our backs we wear.

Where can we begin?
What we want most is a house to live in.

We are sometimes blue,
But we are rich with memories that are true.

If you read this you'll learn that we are poor
We have nothing more.

Thank you for listening to our tale
Please help us where others fail.

Alice Pearson (9)
Drighlington Primary School

Our School

Our school is made of stone,
Our teacher's skin and bone,

She's a fire-breathing dragon
And instead of a car
She drives a wagon.

She likes to loudly shout
She storms and bangs about.

In her garden she has an abandoned pool,
That's why I wouldn't like her as my teacher in our school.

Charlotte Mills (9)
Drighlington Primary School

Holding A Baby

When I hold her in my hands she was kind of cute.
But now she is going toot hoot toot,
She is mumbling a very big lot,
But now she is rattling my new pot.

Now her tummy has started to rumble
Hope she doesn't mumble, mumble, mumble.
She's getting really annoying now.
I wish I could make her moo like a cow.

I gave her some milk it made her happy
But then I had to changer her nappy
Then one day mum came home,
And I was on my own.

So I didn't have to hold the baby anymore,
So I made an apple core.

Lee Gibbons (8)
Haworth Primary School

My Baby Sister

My baby sister is soft,
Adorable and very cute.
When she comes out of the bath
She goes bright red
And smells of baby lotion.
Her skin is very sensitive
It's very soft as well.
When I hold her Mum says,
'She's very delicate,
Be careful not to drop her!'
Her name is Faith.

Kate Foster (8)
Haworth Primary School

My Baby Brother

My baby brother
Is very light
But he has a heavy head
I hold him at night
Before he goes to sleep
His name is Joshua
He smells like red roses
He is my favourite brother.

Jenna Greenwood (8)
Haworth Primary School

My Baby Brother

My brother loves playing with his teddies
He drinks lots of milk.
He was very, very, fat when he came out of mummy's tummy
His name is Jack
I love him a lot,
He feels like a little sheep.

Billie Moran-Whitehead (8)
Haworth Primary School

My Baby Brother

My baby brother likes playing with a pretend bike.
He looked funny when he came out of my mum's tummy
I thought his face was funny because he had lost of freckles,
My mum said that I could hold my baby brother after tea.
After tea I held him
His hands were small.
I loved holding him and he smelt like milk and hospitals.

Katie Cubitt (8)
Haworth Primary School

My Baby Sister

My baby sister sleeps all day.
I held the baby whilst she slept
My baby sister smells like roses,
My baby sister is delicate and fragile.
My baby sister is sweet
Her name is Katie
She breathes heavily while I hold her.
She holds my finger while I hold her
She laughs while I hold her.

Harriet Phillips (8)
Haworth Primary School

My Baby Brother

My baby brother
He is very, very smelly
He smells of milk
My baby brother
Goes bright red when he cries
His favourite toy is a rattle
He is very, very soft
I hold my brother every night
Before he goes to bed.

Joshua Ferguson (7)
Haworth Primary School

My Baby Sister

I was jealous of her
I didn't want her here
She was annoying
But it was nice when I held her
Her name was Lucy
She has a heavy head
She is soft
She has a teddy bear.

Juliet Brown (7)
Haworth Primary School

My Baby Brother

My baby brother is cute
When I hold him I feel his cute nose
He feels squashy
I like to hold him unless he smells
Because he has a full nappy
He is called Max.

Jon Flaherty (8)
Haworth Primary School

My Baby Sister

My baby sister
Is very, very heavy
She smells like roses
When she is cross
Her face crumples up.
I hold her every night.

Michaela Nettleton (7)
Haworth Primary School

My Baby Sister

My baby sister is light and soft
She is sometimes cute and sometimes ugly
When I hold her she goes all red.
My sister, Jessica, has only grown one tooth.

Mum says, 'Be very careful'
When she drops her dodi, pick it up.
Very annoying even when visitors come.

Delicate and fragile
She smells like a banana.

Alexandra Walsh (7)
Haworth Primary School

My Baby Sister

My baby sister is soft and light,
I am allowed to hold my baby sister after her nap
My baby sister, Jessica Rook
When someone holds her she will probably start to cry.
So she will have to go back to my mum,
My sister has only two teeth.

Morgan Rook (7)
Haworth Primary School

Anger

When my friends call me names,
When it's raining and I can't play out.
When my friends fall out with me for no reason.
When people mess with my things and I don't know.
When people push me out of the way,
When my sister hurts me for nothing,
When I have to do my homework.

Laura Parkes (9)
Haworth Primary School

Fear Is . . .

Fear is . . . when my brother jumps out from behind something,
And when my sister pulls a scary face.

Fear is . . . when my mum goes into hospital
And when I hear noises in the night.

Fear is . . . when I stop breathing or have an asthma attack.
Fear is . . . when my mum starts to cry
And my window blows all night.

Jade Hart (10)
Haworth Primary School

Darkness

D ark as Black Beauty
A sparkling star that only we can see
R emember that dark night
K orean nights dark but hot.
N ever can see when you wake up in the night.
E very night at about seven o'clock
S ilence every dark night.
S colding hot in dark Spain.

Hannah Thompson (9)
Haworth Primary School

Fear

Fear is a very cool blue,
Fear smells like the paper of my SATs,
Scary, black spiders climbing up the plug chain,
Worrying in case I get my spellings wrong,
Watching haunted houses on scary movies give me chills,
Fear is a very cool blue.

Laura Kerry (9)
Haworth Primary School

Love

When I get to go to school in a morning I am glad and happy
It is great when I have a lot of homework
Love is bright, beautiful, rosy, red heart
My mum and dad, family and school
Play on computer with friends and family
When I go to school and have lessons like maths
How Miss makes easy work for us.

Bethany Eastwood (9)
Haworth Primary School

Laughter

Laughter is a bright yellow
Laughter is when my mum goes in the freezer and
puts her hands down my back,
I start laughing when my mum tickles me
Laughter is when people start laughing and then crying,
I start laughing when people pull faces at me
I start screaming with laughter.

Vanessa Stead (9)
Haworth Primary School

Laughter

Laughter is when I read a funny poem
Laughter is a funny film like Shrek one and two,
Laughter is when my sister tickles me
Laughter is when someone pulls a funny face
Laughter is when my sister does silly things to make me laugh,
Laughter is when someone tickles my feet.

Amy Paxford (9)
Haworth Primary School

Laughter Is . . .

Playing by the stream and falling in
Chucking my annoying sister in the bin.

Walking up the grass and rolling down,
Having races through the town.

Drinking milkshakes with my friend
Playing a game that will never end.

Cantering along the beach on my favourite pony.
With my friend so I don't get lonely.

Swimming in the sea with the rainbow fish.
In front of my cake making a birthday wish.
That's laughter.

Catherine Wall (10)
Haworth Primary School

My Baby Brother

My baby brother is soft and cute
He smells like baby lotion.
My baby brother is light and delicate.
His name is Finn.
When he smells his face goes bright red.
My mum says I can hold him again
When he's had his tea,
His face is adorable.
He is fragile and small
His hands are tiny
Finn is most special
And cutest of them all.

Amber Sedgwick (8)
Haworth Primary School

Laughter, Laughter, Laughter

Laughter is the colour lilac
It smells like heated chocolate
And tastes like ginger cookies,
Laughter is the funniest of emotions.

Laughter is funny programmes
Like 'Spongebob Squarepants',
A sense of humour
When someone says something funny.

Laughter is comedy like
'Only Fools and Horses,'
When people tell silly jokes,
While watching 'You've Been Framed'.

Jessica Eastell (10)
Haworth Primary School

Holding The Baby

She was howling and yelling,
When they gave her to me.

I said 'I'll calm her down, you'll see!'

I gave her a dummy, and a pat on the back,
'There,' I said, 'that's that!'

She was sleeping peacefully when I put her in her buggy,
As she opened her mouth, I stuck in the dummy!

When I put her in her bed,
Then I came back, she was bright red.

Ella Upton (8)
Haworth Primary School

Holding The Baby

One day my auntie came for tea
She brought my baby cousin, she was glee
My auntie put her on my knee
She wasn't very happy so I fed her
I sang to her but nothing was working.
She was not a very happy baby
My auntie took her off me she was worse
She screamed and yelled some more,
Finally peace and quiet but only for me
I hope she doesn't come until she is older.

Katie Hayes (8)
Haworth Primary School

Anger

Anger is the colour red, it arrives when you're cross
Anger tastes of rough onions. I find anger when I fall out with a friend
Anger feels like a heavy stress
I feel anger for a lot of things
Anger is when you can't do something you want to.

Joe Moore (9)
Haworth Primary School

Feeling Poem Of Laughter

Laughter is when I feel twinkly inside
It happens here, there, mostly everywhere.
It makes me smile,
Not sad or mad just glad.
I have laughter!

Owen Wall (11)
Haworth Primary School

Feelings Poem

Anger is the colour black and smells like rotten eggs
Anger tastes like raw onions and it feels like a boxer is hitting you.
Anger is like a scary film like 'Jeepers Creepers'.
Anger is when people tickle me
Anger is when I get hit
Anger is when people make fun of my hair.

Jonathan Clewes (10)
Haworth Primary School

Laughter

When my cats start running around,
When people tickle me,
When people tell funny jokes,
When people do silly things,
When people do daft things,
When people pull faces.

Alex Palmer (9)
Haworth Primary School

Anger

When my sister's mean to me
When I fall over.
When I miss a penalty
When I get lost
When I have to tidy my bedroom up.
When I get something wrong
When I have to get up.

Zack Robinson (9)
Haworth Primary School

Holding The Baby

He was screaming and yelling didn't like it at all,
I gave him my little finger he stopped all the noise,
He wriggled and kicked the side of the chair still holding my finger,
His eyes were closing he was all still,
Then suddenly he was asleep and so was I,
Z
  Z
    Z
      Z.

Hannah Berrisford (8)
Haworth Primary School

Holding The Baby

She screamed and wriggled I tried to calm her down
I gave her my little finger she wouldn't let go
She started to suck it, her grip got stronger and stronger and stronger
Then pop my finger came out
She started to cry I put her dummy in her mouth
It didn't work
She got louder and louder and louder and louder!
Here we go Mum.

Emily Sargant (9)
Haworth Primary School

Holding The Baby

My mum was holding the baby
He was screaming with anger.

Then my mum gave him to me
He was gurgling at me.
His face got happier and happier and
He was laughing with happiness.

Just then he was that happy he was bouncing like mad.

Andy Rawnsley (7)
Haworth Primary School

My Baby Brother

My baby brother likes playing with Barbies
He looked funny when he came out of my mum's tummy
Because his hair was *gone.*
He smelt like hospital and me
And when they came back I saw him
I loved holding him
I think he is so cute and starts smiling
His head was heavy.

Georgina Walsh (8)
Haworth Primary School

My Baby Sister

My baby sister was born
On November the 30th
She was cute and cuddly
I get to hold my baby sister
She was born in Airedale Hospital
All the family thought she was cute.
Me and my mum put her to bed
She was crying all night
I did get to sleep
I put clothes on that were purple.
I love you.

Laura Gill (8)
Haworth Primary School

My Baby Sister

My baby sister has a habit of annoying me
She is cute and adorable when she is upset
The first time I held my baby sister was yesterday
When my mum finally got her out of the bath.
She felt like the softest baby sister in the world.

Holly Holmes (7)
Haworth Primary School

Laughter Is . . .

Climbing up trees and getting stuck,
Or reading a very funny book
Splashing around in the swimming pool,
Laughing at my sister who's very cool
Dancing in the field, among the flowers
Making shapes in the clouds for hours and hours.

Going to the circus with my friends
On my way home, twisting round the bends
Sat in the garden eating ice cream,
Snuggled up in my bed, having a funny dream.

Zoe Cubitt & Bethany Walsh (10)
Haworth Primary School

My Baby Brother

My baby brother has a heavy head
He looks grumpy when he is smelly
Apart from that he is cute.
His name is Oscar
When I held him I felt proud
He felt soft and cuddly and light.

George Thorpe (9)
Haworth Primary School

Holding The Baby

She screamed and yelled so I said, 'That's enough
I am going to get her dummy and that will shut her up.'
I ran to her dummy and picked it up and when I got back
Gran had calmed her down
I said, 'OK Gran, I'll go and get her bottle for you.'

Ellie Ratcliffe (8)
Haworth Primary School

My Baby Brother

On December 13th,
I stayed at my grandma's
Suddenly my mum and dad came in
My mum and dad came in with a thing
The thing was a little baby
The baby was a little boy
His name was Joseph
I held him before he went to bed
He felt soft and cuddly
I liked him very much
When he was older
He got troublesome and I didn't like it.

Caitlin Sheppard (8)
Haworth Primary School

Holding The Baby

My auntie gave me her baby
She howled at my auntie
When I got her she smiled at me
Because she knew I was going to feed her
When I stopped she glared at me.

Callum Eastell (7)
Haworth Primary School

Laughter

When people tickle me
When people tell jokes
When my kitten goes mad
When children pull funny faces
When people are silly.

Harry Reynoldson (9)
Haworth Primary School

Holding The Baby

She was screaming and yelling when they gave her to me.
They tried to calm her down but it didn't work.
I said, 'Give her to me and I'll try.'
I ran upstairs to get her dummy and stuck it in her mouth
Everyone was silent.

Next thing we knew, when we took her dummy out of her mouth
She was sleeping in my arms.
But then there was a loud crash and she awoke startled.
And started screaming and yelling again.

I put her to bed, so she could calm down
I got her buggy ready to go to town.
When we go to town she started screaming again
Then I said, 'Oh no I forgot her dummy!'

Josephine White (8)
Haworth Primary School

Holding The Baby

She was smiling and gurgling, staring at me,
As Auntie Rachel placed her into my arms,
My face was frowning, I wasn't so sure,
The camera was ready, then suddenly . . .
Flash!

Her face started to crinkle; it had turned bright red,
Then streams of tears running down her cheeks.
She was yelling, yowling then howling.
She was getting louder and louder and louder!
She was about to explode,
So I thrust her into her mum's arms.

Jessie Sargent (8)
Haworth Primary School

My Baby Sister

My baby sister is soft and light
I am allowed to hold her after her tea
Her name is Morgan Snowden
When someone is holding her she falls asleep
Morgan likes to be held
The first time I held her
Her head was heavy
Morgan has one tooth.

Jessica Snowden (8)
Haworth Primary School

The Magic Box

(Based on 'Magic Box' by Kit Wright)

I will put in my box . . .
A big yellow sun
Some blue rain
And a big colourful rainbow
I will put in my box . . .
Fire from the centre of the Earth
The sound of a rock and roll band
And an Xbox 2 from China.

Sam Heyhirst (8)
Hillside Primary School

The Magic Box

(Based on 'Magic Box' by Kit Wright)

In my magic box I will put . . .
Water crashing against the side of the ship,
A creaky grandma's voice.

In my magic box I will put . . .
Waves smashing into each other,
Palm tree's swaying in the breeze.

Rebecca Veira (9)
Hillside Primary School

The Magic Box

(Based on 'Magic Box' by Kit Wright)

I will put in the box . . .
The rustle of wrapping paper on a Christmas Day
Flames from the candles on a birthday cake
The bang of a balloon as it bursts.

I will put in the box . . .
A cat with a furry skin
A crunch of a biscuit from the biscuit tin
A tick from an alarm clock.

Katerina Cervenakova (8)
Hillside Primary School

The Magic Box

(Based on 'Magic Box' by Kit Wright)

In my box I will put . . .
The heat of the sun
The crashing of the waves
In will put in my box . . .
The bubbles of a fish
And the splashing noise of the water.

Azam Iqbal (8)
Hillside Primary School

The Magic Box

(Based on 'Magic Box' by Kit Wright)

I will put in the box . . .
The smell of the flames of a Chinese dragon
The zap of lightning in a thunderstorm
The glistening of the moon reflecting on the sea.

Sam Davies (8)
Hillside Primary School

The Magic Box

(Based on 'Magic Box' by Kit Wright)

In my box I will put . . .
The splashing, crashing waves
And the sun shining on me.

In my box I will put . . .
A skipping rope touring
And a huge bucket and spade.

April Stephens (8)
Hillside Primary School

The Magic Box

(Based on 'Magic Box' by Kit Wright)

I will put in my box . . .
The shine of a glittering star
The smell of a bunch of poppies
The sound of a whistling bird.

Lauren Cunnane (8)
Hillside Primary School

Anger

Anger is red like burning fire
It sounds like pounding bombs everywhere
It tastes like sour milk
It smells like rotten eggs
It looks like smoke
It feels like burning coals
It reminds me of death.

Sophie Brown (8)
Holy Name RC Primary School

Darkness

Darkness is black like a black and red hole sucking out your heart
It sounds like a bull charging at a man
It tastes like rotten eggs
It smells like blood
It looks like a wolf eating a deer
It feels like a dagger stabbing you
It reminds me of death.

Edward Thirkell (9)
Holy Name RC Primary School

Hate

Hate is red like chilli peppers
It sounds like a bomb exploding in my head
It feels like a rough brick wall.
It tastes like sour milk
It smells like rotten eggs
It looks like a monster.
It reminds me of war!

Eleanor Guilfoyle (8)
Holy Name RC Primary School

Fun

Fun is blue like a beautiful blank sky
It smells like sweets, exciting sweets
It tastes like toffee, all brown and sweet.
It looks like a candy shop
It reminds me of my friends.

Garry Mangan (8)
Holy Name RC Primary School

My Nannie

My nanny is as sweet as honey.
My nanny is like a huge cuddly teddy bear
Her hair is like a curly wurly maze.
My nanny is as nosey as a rabbit
She is as soft as a blanket
She talks as much as Little Miss Chatterbox
She is as pretty as a princess
And as comforting as an armchair.

Emily Leadon (9)
Holy Name RC Primary School

The Mad Old Granny Next Door

She's an old rose without any petals
She's an angry cat coming to bite you
She smells of rotten milk
Her teeth are the colour of the sun
She's as mad as a brainless scientist.

Charlotte Stead
Holy Name RC Primary School

Dog

The sharpness of the teeth glisten in the sunlight
Paws ready to pounce hastily it jumped
Its beady black eyes looked nastily at me.
It landed on all-fours.

Liam Armstrong (9)
Holy Name RC Primary School

The Steam Train

The beauty of a steam train
Making its way to Spain
The beautiful art and colour glistening in the sun
Travelling fast to get its job done.

Puffing, puffing out comes the steam
Riding along like a dream
Stop! Step on the brakes
There ready to make the next journey.

Connor Prior (9)
Holy Name RC Primary School

Darkness

Darkness is grey like the stone on a path
It sounds like thunder repeating itself
It tastes like a rotten onion
It smells like mud on fire
It looks like a dark hole
It feels like stone is building up inside me
It reminds me of the biggest baddest storm.

Harry Bates (8)
Holy Name RC Primary School

Darkness

Darkness is orange on a black sunset
Like the beating of my heart
The blood of the sea
Looks like a cat's evil eye
The floor of space
Reminds me of emptiness.

Joshua Burton (8)
Holy Name RC Primary School

Chicken

Chicken pecks around the farmyard,
Moving its head
Merrily, happily, nibbling corn,
Getting fatter and fatter,
Until it's ready for eating.
Lovely! With chips and peas -
Until it's all eaten.
Start it all over again.
Happily eating your dinner,
The best food - in my opinion: chicken.
The noble food.

Ryan Comaish (9)
Holy Name RC Primary School

Grandpa Lou

Grandpa Lou's favourite colour is definitely deep sea blue.
He's always up and about, singing and dancing,
never thinking to shout
He's like a dancing baboon in the light of the moon!
He smells like the sweet fragrance of scented candles.
He's like autumn changing into spring, suddenly turning lively.
He's like a springy chair, ready for anyone to sit on his knee.

Sophie Wood & Rosanna Boardman (9)
Holy Name RC Primary School

Anger

Anger is like flames burning in your head
It sounds like a volcano erupting
It tastes like fire chips
It smells like spicy chicken
It looks like flames tearing down houses
It reminds me of hot lava.

James Price (8)
Holy Name RC Primary School

Hunger

Hunger is yellow like a soul in your tummy
It sounds like a scream high and horrible
It tastes like rotten apple pie
It smells like a graveyard.

It looks like a spirit
It feels like a hot burning fire
It reminds me of deadly nightmares.

Daniel Bouchard (8)
Holy Name RC Primary School

Anger

Anger is red like dragons' fire.
It sounds like a volcano blowing up,
It feels like someone is hitting you on the head.
It tastes like a hot bun in your mouth,
It smells like old milk
It looks like steam coming out of your ears.
It reminds me of volcanos.

Victoria Stead (8)
Holy Name RC Primary School

Anger

Anger is like red-hot fire inside me
It sounds like an exploding volcano
It tastes like sour milk.
It smells like breath.
It looks like a dead body
It feels like lava
It reminds me of death.

Fyn Starr (8)
Holy Name RC Primary School

Happiness

Happiness is yellow
Like the sun shining in the sky
It sounds like the birds singing
It tastes like fresh water
It smells like pretty flowers,
It looks like the people playing on the beach.
It feels like you're still alive
It reminds me of my big sister.

Rachel Farrell (8)
Holy Name RC Primary School

A Skull

A skull lying
On the
Ground silently barely
Noticeable for the inky
Black gloom of its colour
The eyeholes so dark and
Creepy as though they
Want to swallow you whole
When will they ever stop
Staring at me
Glaring staring
Scaring me.

Miriam Forner (9)
Holy Name RC Primary School

Love

Love is pink like a warm feeling in your tummy
It sounds like your heart beating
It tastes like candyfloss you get at the fair.

Natasha Michaelis (8)
Holy Name RC Primary School

Flowers

Flowers come
In different shapes
And sizes with many
Colours to see, in the
Garden they look like a
Rainbow as they welcome
The honeybees.

The petals look
Like tears crying
In the sun
As the leaves
Sway in the
Gentle breeze.

Olivia Bell (9)
Holy Name RC Primary School

Ice Cream

Icy cold refreshing
And sweet, yummy a
Delicious treat. Slurp
It quickly before it
Melts fantastic
Flavours of your
Choice a rain-
Bow of colours
In a cone,
A wonderful
Treat for
Everyone.

Katie Pearson (9)
Holy Name RC Primary School

Smelly Feet

Everyone thinks I'm mad,
But my dad has the smelliest feet in the world.
When I'm curled up in bed
The dreadful smell drifts round the corner into my room
The stench whirls round the room like a tornado
But, making not a sound
Then, it crawls up my nose
Making me inhale the awful pong.
So, no sleep for me
I sneeze while he keeps softly snoring . . .

Footnote: Not true - it's my mum's feet really!

Jessica Barrow (9)
Holy Name RC Primary School

Sweets, Sweets Glorious Sweets

Sweets, sweets glorious sweets
Some are soft and some are chewy
Some are hard and some are gooey.

Sweets, sweets glorious sweets
Lots are sour more are sweet
What's your favourite one to eat?

Sweets, sweets glorious sweets
Chocolate fudge and toffee too
All are my favourite how about you?

Dominic Vertigans (9)
Holy Name RC Primary School

Laughter

Laughter is orange like the warm summer sun shining
It smells like chocolate ice cream trickling down the cone
It feels like butterflies in my tummy
It sounds like children having fun at the beach.
It looks like the sweetie van is parking up here.
I just hope the laughter stays near.

Katie Walsh (8)
Holy Name RC Primary School

Happiness

Happiness is wonderful
It is joy
It is spring air
I love being happy!
It is great,
Lovely
Excellent
Brilliant,
Fab-u-lous!

Thomas Heath (8)
Holy Name RC Primary School

Fun

Fun is orange, like the bright sun.
It sounds like a skilled harp player
It tastes like strawberries and cream,
It smells like cake,
It looks like bubbles,
It feels like a warm radiator
It reminds me of my friends.

Madeleine Durkan (9)
Holy Name RC Primary School

Anger

Anger is like a torpedo
It sounds of explosions
It tastes like gone-off pickles
It feels like an earthquake
It looks like spooky ghosts
It smells like rotten eggs
It reminds me of horror films
It's sudden death
It reminds me of spirits of the dead.

Sam Jones (8)
Holy Name RC Primary School

Fun

Fun is like a great blue sky
It sounds like laughter
It tastes like fresh water
It smells like a swimming pool
It looks like cold ice
It feels like a big diamond
It reminds me of joy.

James Arrowsmith (8)
Holy Name RC Primary School

Love

Love is pink like little love hearts in the sky
It sounds like kisses everywhere
It tastes like strawberries melting
It smells like roses in a flowerbed
It looks like a beautiful princess
It feels like something sweet inside
It reminds me of happy days with my friends.

Cara Greaves (8)
Holy Name RC Primary School

Blue

Blue is the sea where the dolphins like to be.
Blue is the sky where the birds like to fly.
Blue is the water that the animals need to live.
If we didn't have our water I would not be me.
Blue is the diamonds, blue is the jewels,
Blue is the wind flowing as it moves
Blue is the clue, to tell us what to do.
Blue is a flower growing with its power.
Blue means you're cold, lonely and old.
Blue means you're sad, mad and bad,
But only sometimes you can be glad.

Caitlin Belshaw (9)
Hunter's Bar Junior School

Red

Red is the colour of anger or when you have been in a war
Red is the colour of blood when you have been haunted
Red is the colour of electricity when you feel volts
Running through your veins after you have just been shocked
by a red wire.
Red is the time when you look into your memory
And find all your family are gone, only you're left.

Myles Mitchell (9)
Hunter's Bar Junior School

Blue

Blue is as big as a big, basking shark looking for food.
Blue is rain hitting the ground and making crackling noises.
Blue makes me think of juicy grapes watering in my mouth.
Blue is cold, and makes me think of having quietness.

Hamza Saleem (9)
Hunter's Bar Junior School

Week Of Autumn Weather

On Monday shiny conkers came rushing down
They kept slipping out of my fingers and rolling round
On Tuesday I went to the pond on it there was a fine layer of ice
Perhaps it was full of skating mice!
On Wednesday it was so cold my head felt like it was bald,
On Thursday the fog was really thick I couldn't find my dog's stick!
On Friday it was too hot it almost melted my plant pot.

Nadia Jackson (8)
Hunter's Bar Junior School

Week Of Autumn Weather

On Monday the rain came shooting down over the little old town.
On Tuesday the colours of leaves are spread all around.
On Wednesday it's sunny and rainy but very misty in the town.
On Thursday conkers fall from the conker tree.
On Friday there's frost all around and it's snowing like mad.

Elliott Knowles (8)
Hunter's Bar Junior School

White

White is the feel of the soft, clean snow
White is the colour of my fresh clean page
White is the sight of a swirling soft mist.
White is the sound of a plodding polar bear
And the taste of nothing but something,
White is to think without a mind.
White is to feel calm.

Joel Hide (9)
Hunter's Bar Junior School

Week Of Autumn Weather

On Monday it was very cold
The leaves on the trees are going gold.

On Tuesday the wind was really strong
And I did something that was wrong.

On Wednesday it was pouring down
Just when I went to town.

On Thursday lots of leaves came
Off the trees because of the big breeze.

On Friday I stayed in bed
Because I had a very bad head.

Eve Dillon (7)
Hunter's Bar Junior School

Week Of Autumn Weather

On Monday we saw trees with no leaves
Then we looked and saw them scuttling in the breeze.

On Tuesday Jack Frost came to play
He gave us frost for the whole day.

On Wednesday it just had to rain
And I saw some people who had to complain.

On Thursday we had nasty fog
And in the car we crashed into a log.

On Friday we collected conkers
I gave my brother one and he went bonkers.

Ned Cooper (8)
Hunter's Bar Junior School

Wings

If I had wings
I would touch the shimmery rays of the rainbow.

If I had wings
I would taste the crispy crust of the glowing moon.

If I had wings
I would listen to the sound of the sun crisping away.

If I had wings
I would breath in and smell the scent of the sun burning.

If I had wings
I would gaze into the multicoloured space.

If I had wings
I would dream of flying through the moon.

Emma Holliday (8)
Hunter's Bar Junior School

Week Of Autumn Weather

On Monday rain came in a smashing blast
The gutters filled up very fast!

On Tuesday the wind blew in,
It freezes my arms and both my shins.

On Wednesday I slipped on ice and hurt my knee
I wished I were inside with a cup of tea.

On Thursday lots of robins came.
No sparrows though and that's a shame.

On Friday it was very cold
But I stood my ground 'cos I was bold.

Alex Brown (8)
Hunter's Bar Junior School

Week Of Autumn Weather

On Monday I woke up to my surprise all the leaves
Had fallen down as I stomped on them and made a crunch.
On Tuesday there was so much fog I couldn't even see my dog
On Wednesday it was snowing people went tobogganing
On Thursday conkers fell people picked them in their shells.
On Friday there was fog it was so thick
My dog could not find his stick
On Saturday it was so cold I had to stay in my home
On Sunday I could see the acorns on the tree.

Kate Duffy (7)
Hunter's Bar Junior School

Week Of Autumn Weather

On Monday it was windy and the leaves were flying everywhere
On Tuesday it was rainy.
On Wednesday it was frosty.
On Thursday it was stormy
On Friday rain was pouring it down.
On Saturday it was rainy again.
On Sunday it was shining.

Jordan Leitch (7)
Hunter's Bar Junior School

If I Had Wings

If I had wings I would touch the fluffy clouds
If I had wings I would taste a piece of Saturn
If I had wings I would listen to space ships passing by.
If I had wings I would breathe the fiery sun
If I had wings I would gaze at the clashing waves
If I had wings I would dream of walking on Mars.

Matthew Nice (8)
Hunter's Bar Junior School

The Moon Full Of Wonders

Waves of darkness,
Curtains of blue, all lit up by you the moon.
Lined up and orbit, round and round.
All lit up by you the moon.
The lunar light, the yellow beauty,
The milky sphere all adds up to you the moon.
The pearl in the sky is something we call you, the moon.
The mystery of the moon still lies today,
So search for the answer all night!

Ella Marke (8)
Hunter's Bar Junior School

Wings

If I had wings I would fly to the twinkling stars
If I had wings I would touch the clear ice of Pluto.
If I had wings I would taste the blinding sun.
If I had wings I would listen to the cold breeze.
If I had wings I would breathe the light clouds.
If I had wings I would gaze into dark dark space.
If I had wings I would dream of going to Saturn.

Francis Albrow (8)
Hunter's Bar Junior School

Glowing

The moon is always glowing at night
It sparkles all night and it glows like a pearl in the air.
It looks like a cheesy ball
It's brighter and whiter than anything else.

Louise Barker (8)
Hunter's Bar Junior School

Listen

Silence is when you can hear things. Listen . . .
Bees going to work
The flowers squirting the bees
The butterflies singing in a row
The flowers dancing the petal song
The alley cats playing in a band
The butterflies dancing and singing
The caterpillars growing wings
The slugs going to slime school
Leaves floating down to Earth
Sand diving into the sea
The shooting stars colliding with Earth.

Isabel MacInnes (8)
Hunter's Bar Junior School

The Moon

The moon is cheesy and it glows in the dark.
And it shines a lot.
The moon is round like a ball and it spins the Earth.
The moon is very dry.
Astronauts go on the moon with their rockets.

Ramaiz Bashir (8)
Hunter's Bar Junior School

Silence

Silence is when you can hear things, listen . . .
The noise of a frog bouncing around.
The sound of a hare leaping about
And wagging sounds of a newt's tail.

Fionn Cross (8)
Hunter's Bar Junior School

The Moon

The moon is shining every night
It gives people lots of light,
High up in the sky it lives,
It looks like a ball,
I just hope it won't fall.
The stars are its friends.
They live in the sky.
They will never die.
The moon stays still
Most shooting stars go whizzing by.

Esther Gamsu (8)
Hunter's Bar Junior School

Wings

If I had wings I would fly the whole world.
If I had wings I would taste the moon.
If I had wings I would listen to the Earth going round the sun.
If I had wings I would breathe the Earth's core.
If I had wings I would gaze at the sunset.
If I had wings I would dream of a chocolate factory.

Jamal O'Connell
Hunter's Bar Junior School

Wings

If I had wings I would touch Mount Vesuvius
If I had wings I would taste the moon's crust
If I had wings I would listen to the water's edge
If I had wings I would breath the crispy clouds
If I had wings I would gaze all the beauty in the world.
If I had wings I would dream of all the beauty in the world.

Sam Ackerley (8)
Hunter's Bar Junior School

Wings

If I had wings
I would touch the outline of the shimmering moon.

If I had wings
I would taste the fluffy candyfloss clouds.

If I had wings
I would listen to the stars twinkling music everywhere.

If I had wings
I would breathe and sniff the scent of raindrops
falling from cloud to cloud.

If I had wings
I would gaze at the Earth as it twists and turns.

If I had wings
I would dream of sliding down the watercoloured rainbows
one by one.

Ashley Atkinson (8)
Hunter's Bar Junior School

The Moon

The moon is glowing light and dark in the night sky of Heaven.
It is made of cheese and rice as it spins around the Earth.
An astronaut is on the moon stuck in a crater.
The moon is shimmering near the solar system
With its occupants Mercury, Mars, Earth, Neptune,
Uranus, Saturn, Jupiter and Pluto
The moon's best friend is the sun,
Because the sun gives light to the moon.
In the morning the moon swaps places with the sun,
Like swapping a pen to a pencil
When you want to write something.
Now it's time to go to bed because it's morning.

Rebecca Moran (8)
Hunter's Bar Junior School

Wings

If I had wings
I would touch the crystals hanging off Pluto.

If I had wings
I would taste the candyfloss clouds.

If I had wings
I would listen to the sparkling sun shimmer.

If I had wings
I would breathe and sniff the chocolate Milky Way.

If I had wings
I would gaze at Pluto shiver and freeze.

If I had wings
I would dream of walking the stars and swimming the rings of Saturn

Kitty Kendall (8)
Hunter's Bar Junior School

Wings

If I had wings
I would touch the glowing moon.

If I had wings
I would taste the stars.

If I had wings
I would listen to the birds in the sky.

If I had wings
I would breathe and sniff the sun's rays.

If I had wings
I would gaze through Heaven's gates.

If I had wings
I would dream of going through space and landing on every planet.

Lilian Hardie (8)
Hunter's Bar Junior School

Week Of Autumn Weather

On Monday I went to the park where the
crispy leaves crackle under your feet.
On Tuesday I went on a walk and I picked up conkers on the way.
On Wednesday I went in my garden where I saw an empty apple tree.
On Thursday I went to the park again when
the leaves fell on my nose.
On Friday I did not dare go outside, it looked cold and frosty
but when I came outside to my surprise it was hot.
On Saturday it was about 10 degrees.
On Sunday it was so cold, I couldn't take one step.

Harriet Baddeley (7)
Hunter's Bar Junior School

The Moon

The moon is light
The moon is made out of cheese
The moon is round
The moon is in the dark.

The rockets fly up to the moon
The rockets land on the moon.
The astronaut goes on the moon.

Sam Jenner (9)
Hunter's Bar Junior School

Wings

If I had wings I would touch the sizzling rings of Saturn
If I had wings I would taste the twinkling stars.
If I had wings I would listen to the raindrops on the roof.
If I had wings I would breathe the blue air.
If I had wings I would gaze at the sparkling moon.
If I had wings I would dream of touching Saturn.

Oliver Allen (9)
Hunter's Bar Junior School

Week Of Autumn Weather

On Monday the leaves crunched when you stepped on them
they were like cornflakes.
On Tuesday the rain was spitting and the sun was shining.
On Wednesday it was a bit rainy and a bit windy.
On Thursday the trees were swaying side to side and
I found conkers on the ground.
On Friday it was a bit cold and icy.
On Saturday it was very snowy but there wasn't enough
to make snow angels.
On Sunday I made four snow angels.

Ela Bonsall (8)
Hunter's Bar Junior School

Week Of Autumn Weather

On Monday we had a gale and all the leaves went pale
On Tuesday we collected conkers and then I read a book about trees
On Wednesday all the trees shook in the autumn breeze.
On Thursday I did my best to put on my warm yellow vest.
On Friday we had lots of rain and could hear it on the windowpane.
On Saturday my mum didn't let me pay so I made the hay.
On Sunday I did pay but the money didn't stay.

Eleanor Leaney (8)
Hunter's Bar Junior School

Week Of Autumn Weather

On Monday I see leaves fall all in a golden hurry.
On Tuesday I see conkers falling to the ground.
On Wednesday I see a bunny rabbit leaping to the ground.
On Thursday I see trees without lovely little leaves.
On Friday I go for a walk in the lovely Autumn breeze.
On Saturday I picked conkers in the breeze
On Sunday I climbed a tree without leaves.

Charlotte Moulden (7)
Hunter's Bar Junior School

Week Of Autumn Weather

On Monday when I was walking to school,
I splashed on through a little pool.
On Tuesday when I went to the park,
I heard a little doggy bark.
On Wednesday I went rustling through the leaves
And rushing past the bare trees.
On Thursday it was raining conkers,
One hit my head and I went bonkers!
On Friday I got a cold
The leaves were really big and bold.
On Saturday I sat on the frost
My mum got really really cross
On Sunday the sun started to shine through
Jackson hid and I said boo!

Joe Scalisi (8)
Hunter's Bar Junior School

Wings

If I had wings
I would gaze at the sparkle in raindrops.

If I had wings
I would taste the cheesy moon.

If I had wings
I would listen to sizzling Saturn.

If I had wings
I would breathe the midnight air.

If I had wings
I would dream of riding a star.

Eleanor Massey (8)
Hunter's Bar Junior School

Yellow The Sign Of Happiness

Yellow is the colour of a lion cub walking very proud.
Yellow is the season of autumn with crunchy leaves
falling to the ground.
Yellow is the sign of ice cream day with joy and happiness.
Yellow is a walk among the countryside with daffodils tickling your leg
Yellow is the juicy fruit of sour lemons.
Yellow is a walk on a sunny beach with the brownie sand
blending in with the blue sea.
Yellow is the colour of the sun holding a candle
'Do you like butter?' the yellow buttercup asks you in its flowery field
Yellow is the feeling of happiness, kindness and joy.
Yellow is my favourite colour.

Alisha Thompson (9)
Hunter's Bar Junior School

Week Of Autumn Weather

On Monday I see the wonderful shimmering leaves
fluttering off the Autumn trees.
On Tuesday the day of dawn, family crisis instead
of mowing the lawn.
On Wednesday the breeze is nice and cool,
oh, dear my brothers being a fool.
On Thursday I see the autumn's smiley face,
go to the park without a trace.
On Friday we break the leaves instead of making cups of tea.
On Saturday a changed weekend there are lots of leaves
around the bend.
On Sunday there's a slight delay, the children come out to play.

Dana Dorricott (7)
Hunter's Bar Junior School

Green

Green is a slimy frog that jumps from lily pad to lily pad.
Green is spring turning to autumn with the jewelled grass.
Green is a swamp with mud baths and gooey grass.
Green is a leaf in summer with more leaves wherever you turn.
Green is a crunchy and crispy salad.
Green is an apple sour and juicy that crunches every time you bite.
Green is a weed in charge of the garden with its army.
Green is guilty with spikes of jealousy.

Juliette Simpson (9)
Hunter's Bar Junior School

Blue

Blue is a big, shiny dolphin.
Blue is a cold, windy winter.
Blue is a wet, rainy day.
Blue is a tall, shiny building.
Blue is a big, bouncy ball.
Blue is a sour sweet.
Blue is a sweet blueberry.
Blue is cosy and comfortable feeling
Blue is a forget-me-not.
Blue.

Nadra Said (9)
Hunter's Bar Junior School

Week Of Autumn Weather

On Monday it was cold and sunny
On Tuesday the trees shook and all the leaves fell on the ground.
On Wednesday it poured down with rain.
On Thursday there was a hurricane.
On Friday it was boiling hot.
On Saturday it was as cold as anything.
On Sunday in was snowing.

Anina Atkinson (7)
Hunter's Bar Junior School

Yellow

Yellow is a soft fluffy duckling, pretty little thing
Reminds me of spring
Bright summer light, shining yellow,
Beautiful sun gleaming down at me.
Yellow is the Beatles with their yellow submarine.
Yellow, at the tip top of the flame,
The food of yellow is melted, yummy cheese.
Daffodils are yellow planted in the ground,
Bananas are *yellow* and that is that,
Yellow is happiness whispering to me.

Rohan Kon (9)
Hunter's Bar Junior School

Black

Black is a fierce cat on the back of a witch's broomstick
Black is the winter cold and dark
Black is the house of an evil vampire - his jaws long and sharp
Black is a shadow following me about
Black is the raisins inside a small packet
Black is a blackberry in a field of thorns.
Black is the feeling of scary and cold things creeping up behind you.

Brittany Copeland-Booker (9)
Hunter's Bar Junior School

Red

Red makes me think about the gory blood when a war has ended,
Like the silky fur on a baboon's nose,
It makes me think of roses, love and passion,
Red is the colour of a warm flickering stove,
The warm sunset in the evening time,
Strawberries ripening in a field ready to pick,
But most of all the envy, power, the hatred.

Eddie Joe Robinson (10)
Hunter's Bar Junior School

Orange

Orange is a kind furry, ginger cat
Orange is the nightie of summer
Orange is lovely orangey, red sunset
Orange a battery quite low
Orange is a fruit juicy and sweet.
Orange is a plant as nice as could be.
Orange is creamy cheese
Orange is liquid happiness.

Michael Wu (9)
Hunter's Bar Junior School

Blue

Blue is pure shining rivers by a log cabin.
Blue is the chilly wind in a winter's morning
Blue is the smooth frozen winds next to the clouds
Blue is the soft sound of water running.
Blue is the sweet sensation of the taste of fairy cakes
Blue is the creamy colour of the big blue marble we call the Earth.
Blue is the feeling of a happy face.

Monisha Chakravorty (9)
Hunter's Bar Junior School

Yellow

Yellow is a cuckoo bird flying from cage to cage
Yellow is the soothing sun putting out your rage
Yellow is a tasty cheese from all around the world.
Yellow is the gentle sound that keeps your hair curled!
Yellow is a sweet colour that keeps friendship together
Yellow is a calm colour keeping out bad weather.

Ahsan Anderson (9)
Hunter's Bar Junior School

Green

Green is a tiny caterpillar crawling over leaves
Green is the season of spring and brightness
Green is the grass patch in the field
Green is a warm woolly jumper putting it on in winter
Green is sprouts and broccoli with green seeds and leaves
Green is clover swaying in the wind
Green is an apple hanging on a tree
Green is a pear rolling round the table.
Light green is the colour of the sea
Green is a feeling of sadness lying in an empty space.

Hannah Guy (9)
Hunter's Bar Junior School

Yellow

Happiness is yellow like the sun in the sky
And the flowers in the garden.
Happiness sounds like a hummingbird sitting in a tree
Happiness tastes like honey
Happiness smells like lemon and lime
Happiness looks like the warm sunny beach
Happiness feels like a warm funny coat
Happiness reminds me of Christmas.

Joseph Bell, Jack Hookham, Mikey, Asma & Angelina (9)
Hunter's Bar Junior School

Blue

Blue is a shiny, smooth, slithering, jumping dolphin
playing in the water
Blue is the wet, cool, splashing, happy rain.
Blue is the sharp, spiky, cold icicles hanging from the rocks above.
Blue is the icy cold, water in the clear blue sea.
Blue is the pretty, little bluebells swaying in the sun.
Blue is the feeling of calmness.

Rosie Castle (9)
Hunter's Bar Junior School

White

White is a gentle, warm polar bear.
White is a crunchy, fun, soft winter's day.
White is when the tough, hurtful hailstones come.
White is an ice rink full of happiness.
White is like a trapped ice cave.
White is the taste of melting, yummy white chocolate.
White is suspicious and full of wonder
White is the lovely smell of a white rose.
White is cold, damp, freezing icicles.
White is a cold, trapped ice ball in you.
White is a damp, cold feeling.
White is wonder!

Emily Matthews (9)
Hunter's Bar Junior School

Love

Love is red like a lit candle
Love is loud like a heart beating
Love is sickly like Brussel sprouts
Love is smelly like out of date aftershave
Love is ugly like a hippo's bottom
Love is like mouldy squashed tomatoes
Love reminds me of Cadbury milk chocolate.

Calvi Thompson, Mark Eastall, Ellie Chowcat, Louis Protano, Ethan Caris & Naomi Cooper (9)
Hunter's Bar Junior School

Brown

Brown is the colour of leaves
The colour of autumn conkers and sand on the beach
And the jacket and hat of a pet monkey
Brown is animals hunting at night.

Aran Johnson (9)
Hunter's Bar Junior School

Blue

Blue is the whales splashing in the sea
Diving and jumping in the waves
Blue is winter and the cold feeling
When you look out the foggy windows
Blue is the rain the cold miserable rain
The weather that makes you shiver
Blue is the place where I live
And the colour of my cosy bedroom.
Blue is my jumper it keeps me warm and safe
Blue is my blueberry pie, the tasty warm feeling inside me.
Blue is the feeling of the dazzling sky filling up my eyes.
Blue is the blueberries I pick off my tree.
Blue is a bluebell on a greeny shiny stalk.

Justin Wright (9)
Hunter's Bar Junior School

Yellow

Yellow is the burning hot sun
Yellow is a sour, yellow lemon
Yellow is a curvy delicious banana
Yellow is a bright yellow buttercup
Yellow is a colour of the colourful rainbow
Yellow is the spreadable margarine
Yellow is the sight of unbrushed teeth
Yellow is the colour of light
Yellow is the sand on a washed up beach
Yellow is the colour of sweet honey
Yellow is the colour of pollen
Yellow is a flashing lightning bolt.

Swati Kaladagi (9)
Hunter's Bar Junior School

Red

Red is a poppy
Like a still red squirrel
Red is autumn
The light of a red leaf blinding me
Red is warmth
Swarming around me
Red is a chilli
Boiling me to death
Red is the sun
Heating up the earth
Red is the planet Mars
Red smoke billowing round me
Red is anger
Boiling to the brim.

Joe Tudor (9)
Hunter's Bar Junior School

Listen

Silence is when you hear things, listen . . .

Listen to the moon on the shimmering stars.

Listen to the bees eating their sticky honey.

Listen to the plants eating and drinking their water.

Listen to the clouds floating across the greyish sky.

Listen to the birds dropping their feathers.

Listen to the bubbles sticking to the floor.

Listen to the sun changing to the moon.

Listen to the snail gliding across the road.

Adrianna Waite (8)
Hunter's Bar Junior School

Sense Poem

Sadness is blue like a tear from an eye
Sadness is a quiet lake a small corner in the smallest room
Sadness tastes like the darkest moon
Sadness smells like the wettest winter morning
Sadness looks like the darkest sky
Sadness feels like the roughest rock
Sadness reminds me of a gloomy sky.

James Gosling, Alexandra Shirley,
Madeline Gill & Max Dhillon (9)
Hunter's Bar Junior School

Fear

Fear is black like the darkest forest
Fear sounds like a wailing ghost going 'oooh'
Fear tastes like mould and things that are old
Fear smells like sick and things that are ick!
Fear looks like blood dribbling down your hood
Fear reminds me of scary things and scary stories.

Yonis Warsame, Daanish Ahmed, Alice & Isabel (9)
Hunter's Bar Junior School

Sense Poem

Hate sounds like millions of thunderstorms
Hate is black like an evil spirit
Hate smells like smoke coming down a dragon's nostrils.
Hate looks like a bomb from the Sahara.
Hate fears like somebody hammering a pin through your head.
Hate reminds me of people suffering and dying in a war.

Calam McCormac, Lily, Alex, Josef Kent & Aneesah (9)
Hunter's Bar Junior School

Sense Poem

Anger is red like a burning fire
Anger is loud like a roaring lion
Anger is hot and spicy like a red-hot chilli
Anger smells like a burning fire.
Anger looks like a fierce bull.
Anger feels like a red-hot volcano
Anger reminds me of a baby screaming.

Hannah Gagg, Esme Moxley, Asa Stickland, Morgan Ball, Simon Cavan, Lewis Chalmers (9)
Hunter's Bar Junior School

Listen

Listen to a slimy slug sliding through shimmering grass
Listen to the stars twinkling to the moon
Listen to a ladybird crawling across a leaf
Listen to the world spinning around,
Listen to a caterpillar climbing.
Listen to a paper plane flying.
Listen to an insect flying along the road.

William Evans (8)
Hunter's Bar Junior School

Listen

Silence is when you can hear things, listen . . .
Someone working their way through a puzzle
The sun climbing out of bed
A lily pad floating
A feather falling from the sky
A snake sleeping under a log
A cloud easing itself across the sky.

Chloe Schooling (8)
Hunter's Bar Junior School

Listen

Silence is when you can hear things listen . . .

Listen to a tree blowing in the breeze
Listen to an ant quickly eating a leaf
Listen to a frog leaping from lily pad to lily pad
Listen to corn growing in the harvest
Listen to the sound of the wind
Listen to the sound of slugs eating
Listen to a person eating grapes
Listen to a stone rolling down a hill
Listen to a bee telling a story
Listen to a vase being made.

Joe Chantry (8)
Hunter's Bar Junior School

Red

Red is the colour of sweet, tasty strawberries,
Red is the colour of a rose in the garden with a beautiful smell
Red is the season of bright, quiet spring.
Red is the weather of burning yellow, orange, red sun.
Red is the sound of tropical, lively parrot living far from here.
Red is the feeling you get when you're angry and just want to burst.

Ozzy Bill (9)
Hunter's Bar Junior School

Red

Red is the sunrise and reddish sky
Red is a bright prickly rose
Red is love and romance
Red is crunchy apples in the Sunday market
Red is a feeling of warmth and fire
Red is blood when you're hurt
Imagine a world without
Red!

George Bennett (9)
Hunter's Bar Junior School

Listen

Listen to a baby growing,
Listen to a shoe lying on the floor,
Listen to a child staring,
Listen to a balloon going down,
Listen to a painting on the wall,
Listen to a glass of water,
Listen to a baby in China,
Listen to a plant growing,
Listen to a light hanging on the roof of the room,
Listen to the wind blowing open a book.

Katie Grant (8)
Hunter's Bar Junior School

Listen

Listen to night talking to day
Listen to a flower growing
Listen to a spider spinning a web.
Listen to germs spreading on the table.
Listen to your brain thinking
Listen to somebody dreaming
Listen to paint dry
Listen to pastels smudge
Listen to wood rot.

Grace MacIntyre (9)
Hunter's Bar Junior School

Orange

Orange is a warm, flickering, crackling fire,
Orange is the colour of a light bulb fluttering in and out of focus
It is the colour of warm sun,
Orange is the colour of a nice, juicy carrot
Orange is the feeling of confusion and bewilderment.
Orange is the most beautiful sunflower in the garden.

Isobel Blacksell (9)
Hunter's Bar Junior School

White

White is icy cold water
White is fresh and white is clear
White is a furry, soft polar bear
White is a clean white rose
White is a large iceberg
White is the froth on top of a refreshing drink
White is the colour of Antarctica
White is also the colour of this paper
White is a dove and a lily in the valley
White is a cold quiet feeling.

Paul Crawley (9)
Hunter's Bar Junior School

The Grand Entry Of Autumn

Enter autumn in his entire colour
Wearing a coat of golden brown
Embroidered with the threads of sunlight
His tears of frustration with this difficult role

Suddenly autumn notices a change
A cold finger of fog sweeps over the boards.
As autumn exits stage left,
And the cold grip of winter takes centre stage.

Matthew Hill (11)
Meanwood CE Primary School

Spring

S pring is a rabbit hopping all around,
P eacefully jumping around in the grass,
R olling about in the new spring flowers.
I nside, outside, playing hide-and-seek.
N ibbling on the new green shoots,
G iving love to everyone.

Brogan Waters (10)
Meanwood CE Primary School

Autumn

Autumn is a tiger
He watches his prey
He makes the world beautiful
But he's not here to stay.

As he crouches in colours
He fixes his eye
On Mother Nature
And leaves passing by.

With a dropping petal
And a flash of fear
The tiger is coming
Nearer, then near.

The tiger pounces
He's made the trees bare
Mother Nature is crying
As she feels the chilled air.

Siri Basavaraj (10)
Meanwood CE Primary School

Night

Two brown, sullen eyes stared out
Of a cave in woods by the city of thieves
The dark clothed king of night
Glides through a window
Spreading peace and tranquillity.

The night king walks through the wood
After his evening duties
Sleeping in the daylight
Through rain and snow, ice and sleet
He still spreads peace and tranquillity.

Matthew Laurillard (10)
Meanwood CE Primary School

Spring

Spring is a lamb
He's just been born,
Brings life to the world.
With the sunrise at dawn.

Spring is a chick
He twitters in his nest,
He tries to escape
But is told to rest.

Spring is a foal
That wakes in the hay,
He tries to get up,
Because he wants to play.

Spring is the sun
That stretches out his rays,
He gives life to the world,
As he brings a new day.

Hannah Mattinson (10)
Meanwood CE Primary School

I See A Hamster

I see a hamster
As beautiful as could be
He is so soft and fluffy as could be
And he is caramel and white in colour
And he crawls on all-fours
He bangs on his cage trying to communicate
But all he does is keep me awake
He sleeps in the day and then he comes out to play
He is called Cutie and he is one year old
But as I said all that he does is keep me awake!

Rebecca Galea (8)
Meanwood CE Primary School

Night

A safe smile on a sleepy face
Swiftly gliding through the whistling trees
Night's face is a lovely still dreamy face
The sorceress sigh is a gleaming picture
That glitters in the midnight sky.

Silently the sorceress comes into your dreams
And leaves with her glittering sigh.
Stealthily sneaking through windows and doors
The burglar stealing obsessions
What a beautiful sight.

The sorceress returns with her glittering sigh
And covers all of the midnight sky.

Christopher Evans (10)
Meanwood CE Primary School

Autumn

You know when autumn comes because
All the leaves drop down from the trees,
You no longer feel the summer breeze.

The nights start to get darker
This is when you need to wear your parka
It's starting to get nippy,
The ice is getting very slippy.

It's getting near to Christmas now,
Yeah, yeah big wow!
The children go to open their presents
Hoping it isn't a pheasant
That is how you know when autumn comes.

Sophia Hindley (11)
Meanwood CE Primary School

Winter

She slowly falls round and round,
And gently rests on the ground
She glides in her icy sleigh
And rides her horses dressed in grey.

She likes long nights and dark days,
'I hate the sun,' is what she says
Icicles hanging from cave ceilings
No more warmth, it's all cold feelings.

She scoops up all the warmth and heat,
And drops heavy snow at your feet.
She flies across skeleton trees
And freezes everyone she meets.

Then slips into the palace alone
Knowing it's time to go.

Natalie Wood (10)
Meanwood CE Primary School

I See A Dog

I see a dog, it wags its tail
As it is waving to me.

It leaps up and jumps
It moves rapidly
Pale chocolate-brown
Hobbles on three legs
It's got silky chocolate fur
It makes screeching noises like a car.

It moves quickly in the forest
It lies across your legs.

Ashaunté Hamilton-Martin (8)
Meanwood CE Primary School

Night

Her staring yellow eyes glisten in the darkness
Her mouth is like a crescent moon
Her long black dress drifts in the wind
She lives on the moon in the craters of dust.

She's kind and friendly when up on the moon
But down on Earth she's mischievous and cruel
When evening draws near she turns day into night
With the flick of a switch she's nowhere in sight.

Then she goes back to the moon where she lives
She drifts off to sleep in an instant or two
The Earth is in sunshine for the rest of the day
Until she comes back and it all starts again.

Jacqueline Clift (10)
Meanwood CE Primary School

Autumn

Autumn is a squirrel
Racing through leaves
A scarlet red squirrel,
Circling the trees.

The squirrel jumps and hops,
Knocking down leaves
Sending acorns tumbling
Tossing chestnuts down.

He nips chilled fingers
He pinches a cold nose
Exhales a cold mist,
As he settles down for a winter doze.

Andrew Robertson (10)
Meanwood CE Primary School

The Hedgehog

I scramble through the leafy glade
Come? See the patterns I have made
I scatter leaves to left and right
To seek a bedroom for the night.

I tunnel into garden green
At night-time when I can't be seen,
Sometimes people leave me food
Which, I must say, is very good
They also leave me milk to drink
This keeps me alert I think.

My nose is black like patent leather
My spines are strong and spiky feathers
My eyes they shine in the dark
I sleep in holes in an old tree bark.

I know I look so cute to you
But I do have a job to do
I rid the gardens from the slugs
And other little plants and bugs.

If you should see me late at night
Don't pick me up and give me a fright
For I'll roll up in a ball
And hope I won't be seen at all.

Stephanie Turner (10)
Meanwood CE Primary School

The Autumn Dormouse

Autumn is a dormouse
That snuffles around trees
And digs a nest
Getting ready for winter.

Hiding between summer and winter
Dropping leaves of red and yellow
That shine in the fading sunlight
Then crinkle up and die.

Scuttles around,
Between trees,
Gathering in nuts
For his winter store.

Winter comes,
And autumn hides,
In its little nest
Hibernating till next year.

Leah Williams (10)
Meanwood CE Primary School

Patch

I see a big rabbit called Patch,
Patch is playing with his red ball
Patch does bunny hops across the lawn
Patch is light brown with a white patch
He is a round and fat rabbit,
Patch has soft silky fur
Patch makes a twitching sound with his nose
Sleeps all the time,
But Patch died.

Adam Potter (9)
Meanwood CE Primary School

I See A Little Rabbit

I see a little rabbit
I see a little rabbit playing football
I see it running really fast
Brown and white rabbit
It is a small skinny rabbit
Soft fluffy white fur, long lop ears and a long twitchy nose
It yelps when it gets hurt
It runs very fast
It scores a goal.

Tom Madden (8)
Meanwood CE Primary School

A Terrapin In Me

I have a terrapin in me
Splashing playfully in the water
Pretending is it swimming away from me.
The colour of his skin is yellow
The shell colour is sort of a greeny blacky colour
They play really really really joyfully
I love my terrapins.

Callum Raper (8)
Meanwood CE Primary School

The Baboon In Me

I have a baboon in me
Laughing loudly
Quickly swinging
Jumping lightly
Loudly shouting
Running freely
Slowly climbing.

Edward Myhill (8)
Meanwood CE Primary School

The Dolphin In Me

I have a dolphin in me
Friendly bobbing up and down
Playing kindly
Proudly swimming
Jumping high out of the water
Happily clapping
Squeaking loudly

I want to be one of the dolphin's friends.

Hannah Amos (8)
Meanwood CE Primary School

I See A Little Cat

I see a little cat
It creeps into my brother's room
It moves sneakily
Black with white legs
Skinny and tiny
Furry and soft
It makes a noise like miaow
Destroys the sofa
It likes to sleep and eat.

Alex Campbell (8)
Meanwood CE Primary School

I See A Cat

I see a cat
Moving viciously
Black and white neck
It is a rectangle
It is very soft and shiny
It makes a miaow
She hunches her back
She doesn't scratch anymore.

Oliver Campbell (8)
Meanwood CE Primary School

I Have A White Eagle In Me

I have a white eagle in me
Spying secretly
Proudly gliding
Ravenously munching
Standing quietly
People admire it
They want to fly with it
It respects them
It glides in circles looking for its prey.

Conor Turner (8)
Meanwood CE Primary School

I Have A Cat In Me

I have a cat in me
Playing happily with her tail
Running swiftly in a circle
She's the colour of a tortoiseshell
She's long and thin like a ruler
Her skin is as fluffy as a chicken's feather
She purrs annoyingly at the door
Waiting at the door to be let out today
I love my cat.

Anna Howard (8)
Meanwood CE Primary School

I See Alfie

I see a dog
Jumping around in his green garden
He is brown and white
He is round like an egg
He barks like mad
Jumping and playing with his balls
That's our Alfie.

Thomas Dickinson (8)
Meanwood CE Primary School

Eagle

I have an eagle in me
Waiting watching
Swooping slowly
Round in circles higher
Into the sky higher
Then through the trees suddenly
Down, down to its prey
Suddenly it strikes
Crunch, crunch.

Ben Hills (8)
Meanwood CE Primary School

I Have A Mouse In Me

I have a mouse in me
Scurrying and sniffing,
Aware of what's happening
Squeaking loudly,
Eating cheekily,
Munching chocolates
Being quiet and noisy at times
Others try to make me squeak.

Lucy Turner (8)
Meanwood CE Primary School

I've Got An Owl In Me

I've got an owl in me
It sits on an old oak branch
Quietly thinking
Watching the wood
Determined to find what it wants
Not making the slightest noise
Looking for activity and movement
People want to shoot it.

Luke Heppenstall-West (8)
Meanwood CE Primary School

I See A Cat

I see a cat as small as ten little rats
Prowling the street at night
Slowly and extremely smoothly
Blacker than the night sky,
Padding like a white polar bear,
Its skin is white as a polar bear
Miaowing in the moonlight
Walks like a black figure fading into dusk,
When the cat runs into the glorious sunset.

Joshua Milsom (8)
Meanwood CE Primary School

I Have A Guinea Pig In Me

I have a guinea pig in me
Squealing very loudly and noisily
Slowing chewing on fruit and veg,
Running quickly in big and small circles,
Feeling very sad when people don't want to play with him
Hardly trying to be as long as my friends can be
Trying viciously to get some sleep
People want to stroke it.

James Lockley (9)
Meanwood CE Primary School

I Have A Dragon In Me

I have a dragon in me
Gliding gently through my body
Living peacefully,
Staying quietly,
Awakening silently,
Moving swiftly,
People laughing with envy
And I react calmly.

William Houghton (8)
Meanwood CE Primary School

I See A Dog

I see a dog
Sitting patiently by his owner
Suddenly he darts away as quick as a car
He's the colour of dark brown chocolate
His body arches like a tunnel
His fur is short and furry like a horse
He erupts a deep and loud bark
He fetches the ball when he's been told
This is the life of Sam the dog.

Suubi Hope (8)
Meanwood CE Primary School

I Have A Dolphin In Me

I have a dolphin in me
It's chatty and cheeky,
It's playful and friendly,
It's silly and mischievous,
It's quite strong and quite clever
It's a very good swimmer
People want to be friends with it,
But it prefers to be alone.

Kyle Bell (9)
Meanwood CE Primary School

I Have A Dolphin In Me

I have a dolphin in me
It jumps up out of the sea,
Squeaking loudly
Swims in the sea splashing a lot,
Chatting to each other in the ocean,
Playing in the waves,
Making lots of games,
People think they're great.

Laura Challinor (8)
Meanwood CE Primary School

I See A Guinea Pig

I see a guinea pig
Eating his greens quickly
Running around happily,
Toffee brown and creamy white
Round and fat like a ball,
One rosette on his whole body
Squeaking noisily to his mate,
Sleeping in warm corners
That's Toffee.

Rachel Woods (8)
Meanwood CE Primary School

I See A Kitten

I see a kitten
Purring loudly when it's being stroked
Running wildly looking for food
Black as night and white as clouds
Thin and long, you can feel its skeleton under its soft skin
'Miaow,' says the cat when you feed it
Sneaking into the bedroom to sleep
Whiskers that's his name.

Lauren Wall (8)
Meanwood CE Primary School

The Lioness In Me

I have a lioness in me
Proudly and quickly running
Through the sun
Quickly chewing and proudly
And quickly
Proudly roaring cheekily to herself
Getting excited
Just like me.

Rose Drury (8)
Meanwood CE Primary School

I See A Dog

I see a dog
Sleeping lazily in my bed
It walks quickly on four legs
Its head is black and its body is brown, white and black
The dog is small like a cat
Its fur is as smooth as ice
He opens his mouth wide and barks loudly
My dog whines quietly when he is hungry
My dog is one of a kind.

Josh Finn (8)
Meanwood CE Primary School

I Have A Bushbaby In Me

I have a bushbaby in me
It likes climbing trees,
Quietly hiding
Gently cuddling her mum
Cheekily playing
Sleeping silently in the dark
People smile warmly at me
This makes me feel happy and warm to them
Their mums and dads think they're cute.

Eleanor Moreland (8)
Meanwood CE Primary School

The Winter Lady

A lady with a white cloak
Her face is as white as snow
Shoots an icy look
And throws a cold stare
Her nose as sharp as an icicle
The wind blows her long white hair.

Martin Perry (10)
Meanwood CE Primary School

I Have A Dolphin In Me

I have a dolphin in me,
Who swims like a mini fish
In the sea, being friendly
To other dolphins in the valley
She jumps high from the sea into the ocean
She squeaks and says come on play with us and have fun
She is playful as can be.

And that is Francis the dolphin.

Avanda Peverill (8)
Meanwood CE Primary School

I Have An Insect In Me

I have an insect in me
Building and building soundlessly
Being stamped on
Quietly scurrying around
Thinking hard
Gluing anything
Always working
But always let down
That's me.

Liam Budler (8)
Meanwood CE Primary School

Night

The goddess of night as pretty as love
As powerful as a sorceress
Her power brings the darkness to her feet
Her glittery face summons a star
Swiftly gliding through the night
Giving dreams to all that might
Need a dream to take them through
The slumber she has brought.

Samuel Johnson (10)
Meanwood CE Primary School

I Have A Cheetah In Me

I have a cheetah in me
Snoring loudly
With smelly breath
Its roar is as loud as a jet engine
Looking carefully for deer
Sneaking quietly past hunters
Climbing up rotten trees dangerously
It runs as fast as it can
It hunts in the creepy jungle
People want to catch it.
I don't like it
It scares me.

Joseph Walls (8)
Meanwood CE Primary School

Summer

Summer bathes in the sun
Summer floats in the breeze
Summer mows the grass
Summer blows the trees.

Summer enjoys the warm
Summer dives in the pool
Summer plays in the park,
Summer is looking cool.

Daniel Howells (10)
Meanwood CE Primary School

Captivity

His lips quivering, as his big bulging eyes fill with tears
Lost as a soul wandering for freedom
Silently and slowly as a snail climbing up the tree
As they wander for food at night to see if there's any left behind.

They curl up in their leafy bed
Crying themselves to sleep at night,
As the koalas know the children laugh
As the koalas know that in the morning they're in for a big *fright!*

The children rattle and bang the cage,
They give a little groan
They really want to bite or claw them just to make sure,
But what they really want is just to be loved.

The children throw sticks at them just to wake them up
The screaming and bellowing children shout at the koalas
Koalas just think, *shut up!*
They want to roar but nothing comes out.
As they know the next morning the children scream and shout!

His soft fluffy skin is not what it used to be,
Now it is fading
Their ears are drooping sadly
In the wild that's where it wants to be.

He moves around his dark, dusty cage,
Until his food comes,
He drags himself around the cage
Trying to break through.

Will his happy life ever be the same?
The master comes to look around the cage
The koalas look at him in shame.

Hannah Williamson (10)
Pudsey Lowtown Primary School

The Miserable Tiger

Sadly I saw the saddest tiger in the world
As I stared in horror
The tiger wept in the sun as it burnt him
The people laugh in happiness.

I saw the tiger throwing its face in the terrible food
I look at the food
It looked like mud
What a pig would eat.

I saw the tiger drag itself around
The tiger roared for freedom
I cry as the people laugh like they never laughed before
I ran in horror
I tried not to look back, the tiger was in pain!
I had to go back
I smiled at the tiger
It smiled back.

Lauren Leung (9)
Pudsey Lowtown Primary School

Captivity

Whilst I was at the zoo I saw a kangaroo
It kicked the cage, the cage wouldn't break
He bounced and bounced, he tried and he tried
He kicked and kicked but it just wouldn't break.

He moaned and moaned and moaned and moaned
He tried to smash it one more time
And boom the cage smashed open.

Joshua Martin (9)
Pudsey Lowtown Primary School

Captivity For The Moaning Giraffe

As the giraffe strolled across the cage
On feet as wobbly as a vibrator,
Eyes as red as a sore thumb,
At a cruel young age.

Hair as wet as a tap
Heart as sore as a trapped finger
Feet wet with his tears,
Mouth as dehydrated as a fish that isn't in water.

Trailing around the cage as slow as a slug
Back as circled as a hedgehog
Feed dragged around the cage
Legs as stiff as a stone.

Thinking, *get me out of here*
Get me away from the leather wipe,
Thinking, *I can get through this.*

Sophie Paynter (9)
Pudsey Lowtown Primary School

Captivity The Poor Monkey

The poor little monkey jumped from tree to tree
Finding all the bananas but he could not find any
He fell to the floor with sweat dripping from his head
Jay whipped up the tree to find his best friend Bill
But Bill wasn't there.

So he wandered off crying and whimpering for freedom
So Bill came over and Jay ran away from Bill
Bill couldn't be bothered to run after Jay so Bill stopped
Jay burst into tears and fell asleep.

The next morning Jay woke up with a bunch of bananas in front of him.

Melissa West (9)
Pudsey Lowtown Primary School

Captivity The Ostrich

When I was a little chick,
Flapping my wings when proud,
Living freely in the countryside
Jogging, running and dancing round and round.

But now I'm just an old ostrich
Roaring with a ferocious cry,
Everyday is a struggle,
And people force me to fly.

A mournful life like mine with nothing but claustrophobia
Or maybe a few sweats of pain,
If I could just get out of here,
I would cry with grace.

I squeal for my dear brother
In a high-pitched screech,
I cry and cry with devastation
But they were too far out of my reach.

I threw my chain against the bar,
But it didn't make me better,
All I want is to be free,
Suddenly I saw a badge on my neck
I don't believe it, I'm called Heather.

Alexander Brush (9)
Pudsey Lowtown Primary School

Captivity

I was going to see a magic show
As a dragon roared flaming fire which melted all the snow,
I saw a magnificent unicorn
With a beautiful golden horn,
But when I looked very close
I almost turned as white as a ghost
For I'd just seen a horse in disguise
It dragged itself around
I thought it would be wise
For that dragon to reach the ground,
And then I just realised it was an eagle in a suit
Tears streamed down its cheeks and it was no longer scary
But very, very cute.

I saw an evil goblin
As it pranced in shade so dim
I saw a fierce giant tramp
With its eyes so wet and damp
I realised that goblin was just a lizard in clothes
And it looked so desperate to break free,
The tramp was just an ape with its hair made of damp rose,
It was silent as a little buzzing bee.

Zoe Bambrook (9)
Pudsey Lowtown Primary School

Captivity Panda

I saw a panda in the zoo
Roaring at the jungle in front of him
Eyes dropping with tears
The panda dragged itself around the cage.

Up in the cave above
Is a whining and hurting panda
Roaring in anger
Trying to think of a way to get free.

Eating on his bamboo slice
Staring at the jungle
Slurping his warm, dirty water
Whilst moaning to his friend.

Is it true that the panda will get free?
Please let him free
Or please let him go?
Let him go now!

Taylor Heaps (9)
Pudsey Lowtown Primary School

The Unloved Elephant

The unloved elephant was sat on the cage floor in pain
It rose its trunk, the noise it sounded like a lion
Tears falling like a waterfall
He stood tall and walked over to the corner.

It wrapped its trunk around the bar and started to shake
It was trying to escape; the zookeeper came and whipped him
He fell to the ground in hunger or pain
I never saw him ever again!

So now I know that treating animals wrongly is bad
I will never go again.

Jack Agate (9)
Pudsey Lowtown Primary School

Unloved Lion

The lion was roaring in pain
With tears in its eyes
Looking like it is claustrophobic
No one to care for him.

He screeched in hunger
And collapsing through dehydration
Whimpering from being mistreated.
And with scars all over its face from his master's whip.

He cried with terror
With no one to care for him or love him
He dropped to the floor sadly
He looked unkempt.

The tragic lion fell to the floor
He looked really annoyed
He roared loudly
Saying, 'Someone, please help me.'

He collided with the iron bar trying to whack them down
After he throws himself all over
And meanwhile roars in pain.

Jake Thornton (9)
Pudsey Lowtown Primary School

Captivity The Falcon

The surf in the moonlight
The glide in the sky,
Also always sparkle like gleaming glitter.

It squeaks for freedom like rain and thunder clashing together
Its colourful sparkling tears dropping from his outrageous eyes
Plus they are beautiful, glittering, gleaming, gorgeous body.

It will swoop down if it sees its juicy prey
Then swallow its prey stretching its mouth like rubber
They all are so fast in the air.

Bradley Johnson (9)
Pudsey Lowtown Primary School

The Whimpering Tiger

One day I strolled to the zoo,
I was going to see a tiger,
With really sharp teeth,
Oh! I'm so excited!

When I go to the tiger
How much pain it was in,
Everybody was laughing at him,
But I was not.

He was trailing his feet around behind him,
As slow as a baby snail
Its eyes were full of water
Like a 10 foot deep lake.

I wanted to cry and cry until I burst into tears, all day long
Would that animal ever be set free?
Would it? Oh, please let that tiger go!

Its food was just a wet floppy fish
And a little drop of water,
It wanted to have freedom forever
Just a little time out of the bars.

Alice Whiteley (9)
Pudsey Lowtown Primary School

Poor Little Tiger

The poor little tiger in a cage miserable and unhappy
Next door a seal so loved and so happy,
Still the wailing wouldn't end it wailed and wailed.
But then a rock flew at its head
Poor little tiger.

The poor little tiger looking like it's claustrophobic
Little children not seeing the painful, wet, sad, hurt eyes.
Only adults can see the pain in the little tiger's eyes
But little tiger daydreaming of woods
Love and happiness.

Still the tiger dreams
It thinks, *what is out there?*
What is out there?
It dragged itself round the cage and whimpered its heart out
Poor little tiger
It wanted as much freedom as it deserved.

No it didn't work, it wondered and wondered,
What is out there for a tiger?

Alex Parker (9)
Pudsey Lowtown Primary School

Bear Captivity

It feels angry like a lion
Feels like it's dehydrating
Feeling glum and disgraceful, sadness.

Moving slower than a snail,
Banging the metal bars,
Trying to search for water everywhere
Dying in pain and slowly.

It's whimpering is like crying
Its tears dropping, filling it up,
No one is looking after him,
Trying to build up a bit.

It looks like it's a floppy toy,
It has to drag its feet with him.
Actually pulling his whole body in tears
Never ever wants to die in that disgraceful cage.

The old wiry bear feeling hungry, mournful
Tired dragging his weak back legs and then collapsing in pain,
A memory shot back to his head feeling free,
Running in the beautiful nature, but now in the solid metal bars.

The bear is feeling very, very weak
It has lost lots of water from his body.

Hayley Martin (9)
Pudsey Lowtown Primary School

Captivity

An animal in captivity
A creature in the zoo,
Maybe a lion, suppose!
It's outrageous, devastating, disgusting, he must feel aggrieved.

The sadness in his sore, red, mournful eyes
Meant nothing to the zoo visitors
Its growl was weak and feeble
As would be a rabbit's imitation.

The poor creature
Clawed at his room,
His room made of metal bars,
But not for long, with that crumb of food, how could you?

Are we its friend or enemy?
He doesn't know,
He hasn't seen the world,
All he knows is we are foe.

Its mane was extremely dry, tangled, tattered and
the hair fell out rapidly.
His skin was shrivelled
It would be, for he is dehydrated
It limped towards its weekly dish of meaty crumbs.

He dreamed to sprint, to race
With the pride
He wanted to get
Revenge on those who guffawed at him.

Why do people chuckle at him
When he cries, trembles and groans?
It's very cruel
An animal in captivity
A creature in the zoo.

Jade Dhesi (9)
Pudsey Lowtown Primary School

The Blacklash Beaver

Whilst visiting the zoo, a day in June,
Face mournful
A zookeeper was playing a tune
Screeching the place down.

It's whacking on the side of the cage
All humans thinking
What an angry beaver
Wanting to leave the zoo!

Almost collapsing with the pain
Also dehydrating and very, very hungry
Badly hurt with scars all around his body
Thinking he's not popular at all.

At 2.30pm
The zoo was nearly empty from the horrible creature,
Never going to go back,
Because of that little ignorant beaver.

Jade Chadband (9)
Pudsey Lowtown Primary School

Kangaroo

While I was at the zoo
I saw a kangaroo
Tears dripping slowly from her eyes
Whispering to her little joey as slowly as she can.

She's nearly having to do little jumps
Sobbing as she's going over the little humps
Feeling lots of happy thoughts
Hearing lots of strange noises too.

She looks quite enormous and strong,
And also has a little pong,
As they crawl around and in the summer heat
They try to find something to drink and eat.

They lay around in their cage
Even though they are a young age.
She gets a tingling feeling; she's going to get hurt.
She hardly has any friends.

Lucy Gordon (9)
Pudsey Lowtown Primary School

Captivity

While visiting the zoo,
I saw, a sad
Elephant,
He gazed at me with a tear in his eyes.

It dragged itself around
Mournful,
Against the keeper,
It fights, for freedom.

Fence and chain,
Tag and bar,
Heart like a tiny feather
Wrecking and pulling on the trees,

It wailed no louder than a mouse,
Collapsing in pain,
All the children laughed
Would it find freedom?

It was peanuts
But he didn't care
Its wrinkles were helpless
I saw it at the zoo.

Rachel Chadband (9)
Pudsey Lowtown Primary School

Captivity

The old elderly bear feeling hungry, mournful and tied
Dragging his tied wire at the back of him
Then collapsing with pain that split second
He had a flash back seeing himself running freely.

Out of the cage running into the beautiful nature
The bear feeling angry with himself
Getting him into the cage
The tears dropping down like rain.

Moving slow like a snail
Banging against the metal bars roaring
With a shock of pain trying to find a drop of water.

Its cold nose freezing to death
No one to see
No fun, no food and no water.

Looking dreadful, a frozen nose
Eyes half open.

Jack Whiteley (9)
Pudsey Lowtown Primary School

Monkey

I saw a poor little monkey at the zoo
It's eyes filling up with tears
As it suddenly dropped in pain.

It was slowly lolling from one place to another
Wondering what it would be like to be free,
As it was crying like a lost child for its family.

Awaiting freedom to come to its eyes
Because if you looked deeply in his eyes
You would see big trees, and a family to care for him.

All that monkey did was perform all day
And get just a piece of fruit.
And as it performed it moaned in agony,
So next time think when you complain about your food
Just think about the poor monkeys out in the world
So please let them *free!*

Lauren Drake (9)
Pudsey Lowtown Primary School

Captivity Orang-Utan

I saw an orang-utan at the zoo
Cowering slowly behind the cage,
With its brother cowering too
With not much and growling in rage.

It felt sick, angry and sad
With tears trembling down its eyes
It was growling fiercely like mad
In its fur lay tics and flies.

It made grumbling noises and groans,
It was old and 7 years of age
With collapsing noises and moans
Lying in its horrendous cage.

Emma Lokuciejewski (9)
Pudsey Lowtown Primary School

Emerald Stones

The stepping stones to Heaven
Glow like an emerald
With a core of fire
Deep in a cavern

The stepping stones to Heaven
Make you feel like an Emperor
Holding a sceptre and wearing a
Crown of gold littered with diamonds

The stepping stones to Heaven
Are as smooth as a diamond
Tended to by
God himself

The stepping stones to Heaven
Are so beautiful
They appear to be carved by angels
Of the highest rank

The stepping stones to Heaven
Are as old as the God who created
The world
In seven days

The stepping stones to Heaven
Are as minute as a Titan's fist
That is shrunk
One hundred times

The stepping stones to Heaven
Are greater than life itself.

Jonathan Gillespie (10)
St Joseph's RC Primary School, Rossington

Jennifer G

Jennifer
Her eyes twinkle like sapphires
Jennifer
Her skin as bright as peach
Jennifer
As smart as a VIP
Jennifer
Her hair as gold as the flaming sun
Jennifer
She's over the moon all the time
Jennifer
She thinks she's talking to a brick wall
Jennifer
'It's raining cats and dogs'
Jennifer
Her jewellery glistening like golden stars
Jennifer
She's warm hearted like an angel
Jennifer
Never boring like a tortoise
Jennifer
Her lips, red like cherries
Jennifer
Active like a computer
Jennifer
She's my best friend!

Ashleigh McMenamin (9)
St Joseph's RC Primary School, Rossington

Impossible Places

'Guess where I've been?'
'Where?'
'To the moon and back!'
'Grow up and get your head out of the clouds
'Cause dinner's ready!'
'Oh Mum!'

'Guess where I've been?'
'Let me guess could it be perhaps the moon?'
'Oh Mum, don't be daft you know people can't go to the moon!'
'So where did you go?'
'I orbited the Earth!'

'Guess where I've been?'
'Where?'
'I've been to dinner with Queen Victoria!'
'But she's dead!'
'I went back in time!'

'Guess where I've been?'
'Where?'
'I slayed a dragon for the Queen!'
'Did you?'
'Uh huh!'

'Guess where' I've been?'
'Where, hold on somewhere impossible I bet'
'Yes, where no one else would dare to go'
'Where?'
'The compost heap in the backyard!'

'I have news for you!'
'What Mum?'
'I've been to the end of the world and back for you!'
'But why?'
'Because I adore you so much!'

Zoe Forbes (9)
St Joseph's RC Primary School, Rossington

A Deep Dark Dungeon

In a deep dark dungeon
There lived a big black dragon
With a mighty roar.

In the deep dark dungeon
There lived a wicked witch
With a mighty voice.

In a deep dark dungeon
The witch and the dragon
Kept a deep dark secret.

In the deep dark dungeon
The secret was a beautiful princess
With the voice of an angel.

In a deep dark dungeon
The princess sang
All day long.

In a deep dark dungeon
A prince heard a tuneful echo deep
In the cave, the voice of the princess.

In a deep dark dungeon
The prince slayed the dragon
And killed the witch.

In the deep dark dungeon
The princess was rescued
By the handsome prince.

The prince and princess walked out of the deep dark dungeon
Into the moonlight night and lived happily ever after.

Abbie Woodward (9)
St Joseph's RC Primary School, Rossington

Fairy Tales And Fantasies

The moon,
Shimmers,
Like a diamond ring,
In Mum's jewellery box.

The moon,
Sparkles
Like a star,
Twinkling in space.

The moon,
Is magical,
Like a stepping stone,
Leading to fairy tales and fantasies.

The moon
Gleams,
Like a silver crown,
Among a million daisies.

The moon
Shines,
Like a friendly face,
In the dark scary night.

The moon,
Is like a pearl,
Lying in the dark ocean
Of the sky.

Mary-Anne Hunter (10)
St Joseph's RC Primary School, Rossington

A Stepping Stone

The moon glows like a light bulb
It is like a stepping stone to another world
It is a great sight your eyes are attached to
When you look at it you see a rabbit
Jumping up and down
It's the bringer of night and day
A guardian angel watching over us all night
It is better than any planet
As white as snow
As magical as a magician
As pretty as a flower of a rainforest
Like a frisbee thrown up into space
By a playful giant
It is so bright
Everyone stops and stares
If you could keep it people would love to
People faint when you look at it too long
If there was no moon
Life would be so dull
Just thank God for the moon
It is great and free.

Thomas Gillespie (9)
St Joseph's RC Primary School, Rossington

The Ugly Witch

A mouldy-faced witch,
In a hideous castle,
A swoosh of a broomstick,
The floorboards creaking . . .
The door's opening and shutting,
The skeleton's grinning with laughter,
The wind howling through the windows,
Suddenly there was a scream in the distance!
And then she woke up.

Abigail Bowden-Shaw (9)
St Joseph's RC Primary School, Rossington

Jewels

A creamy milky pearl on an
Expensive necklace draped around
The queen's bloodless neck.

A fiery red ruby
Hidden in a shell beneath the salty ocean.

A minty green emerald
Slipped into a shell of gold
And made into a precious expensive earring.

A transparent sparkling diamond awaiting discovery
In a dark gloomy mine
Lying silently and patiently
Like a cat watching its prey.

An amethyst pretty and feminine
Set in a ring of nine carat gold.

Jessica Mould (9)
St Joseph's RC Primary School, Rossington

The Mad Wizard

Deep in the dark, dark forest,
There was a very scary wizard,
With a long long beard.

He's turning trees into flying pigs,
Turning knights into nuns,
And turning ghostly ghouls into tools.

He's pulling out his own hair,
He makes you really stare,
He's jumping up and down,
Like he's just got a gold crown,
I think he's gone absolutely bonkers.

Peter Duhig (9)
St Joseph's RC Primary School, Rossington

Moon Shine

The moon lights up the night sky,
Like a thousand Christmas lights on a pine tree.

The moon shines over the world
Like an ancient pearl around Queen Elizabeth's royal neck.

The moon watches over us
Like a guardian angel in a jet-black sky.

The moon brings in the long nights of winter
Every night it's there
Even when we're sleeping
It's never ceasing energy
And never lets us down!

The moon:
Half moon
Full moon
New moon
Each has different personalities
Like different people except we know
It is always the same moon.

Hannah Black (9)
St Joseph's RC Primary School, Rossington

Our Satellite

The moon glimmers in the starry night,
Like stardust on a jet-black
Sheet of canvas.

Our moon shines like an
Illuminated light bulb,
In a dark, empty room.

The moon is as circular
As a glass,
That has just been blown.

Our satellite is speckled
With craters like
Sparkles from a firework.

The moon is a stepping stone,
For Martians and
Extra-terrestrials.

Yes, the moon is a truly,
Wonderful
Thing.

Harvey Ellis (11)
St Joseph's RC Primary School, Rossington

What A Magnificent Moon

The moon
Is rough and bumpy
Like an old brick
Cemented into a Victorian house.

The moon
Is milky white
Like a fresh saucer of milk
Ready for a cat to lick away.

The moon
Glows
Like a firefly
Hovering in a cloudless sky.

The moon
Has loads of faces
Sometimes it smiles
And sometimes it frowns.

The moon
Is circular
Like a clock on a wall
Working nine to five.

The moon
Is magnificent
He lights up the sky!

Samantha Moorhouse (10)
St Joseph's RC Primary School, Rossington

What If?

What if
People could fly
Like vultures circling their prey
On a dry, dusty desert floor?

What if
Animals could talk
Like a secretary chattering on the phone
In a cluttered and messy office?

What if
There was no gravity
And people drifted away
Like a balloon escaping
Into the depths of space?

What if
People could breathe in water
Like a shark gliding
On the dark seabed?

What if
Aliens visited Earth
Like astronauts travelling to the moon
In a space shuttle on their epic journey?

What if?

Laura Greenaway (11)
St Joseph's RC Primary School, Rossington

The Moon

The moon
Shines,
Like a piece of kitchen foil,
In the steaming hot oven.

The moon
Lights
Up the starless sky
At ten to midnight at night.

The moon
Floats,
Like a beach ball in the sea,
Being hit by waves every minute!

The moon
Appears
In the night,
Like the bats and the owls.

The moon
Glimmers
Up in space,
With the shining stars.

The moon
Sparkles
Like a shimmering diamond,
On a sparkling gold ring.

The moon
Glistens
Like glitter on a party dress,
Or a sparkling pencil or pen.

Without the moon we wouldn't we able to
See at night, be thankful for the moon.

Chloe Murdoch (10)
St Joseph's RC Primary School, Rossington

My Secret Friend

He's as joyful
As a clown
At an entertaining circus.

He's as funny
As a comedian
On a TV programme.

He's as fast
As David Beckham
At taking penalties.

He's as imaginative
As JK Rowling
Writing a Harry Potter story.

He's as friendly
As a pet dog
Kissing a baby's soft cheek.

He's as creative
As Leonardo Di Vinci
Painting Queen Victoria.

He's as thoughtful
As a soldier that
Swore an oath to protect you.

He's as handsome
As Orlando Bloom
In Pirates of the Caribbean.

He's as playful
As a cat
Ripping up its favourite ball of wool.

Can you guess who
I'm thinking of?

Charlotte Watson (10)
St Joseph's RC Primary School, Rossington

Mystery Women

Her hair shines
Like
A golden sunset
On a warm summer's night.

She has a face
Like
An angel's face
Singing loud in the heavens.

Her voice
Is as soft
As a cat's purr
Roaming through the night.

She's a mystery woman
As gentle as
A fairy
Casting a kind and loving spell.

Her dress
Shimmers
Like golden jewels
On the Queen's crown.

Abbey Hinder (10)
St Joseph's RC Primary School, Rossington

Midnight Kitten

In the deep darkness of
The pet store, the
Small kittens were taken away,
All except one.
Just one.
As small and as timid as a mouse
The kitten trembled
In the night with a coat of pure
Midnight.
Now . . .
The sun's out at least
Time to dry her tears.
Then a woman . . . with a family.
She tried to act happy, hoping they would like her.
No hope, they're only hopes, their only
Words were 'What a rat'
Hours passed.
Then another woman . . . she was younger
The kitten didn't try, knowing of no hope, but
She was smiling like a Cheshire cat, then a friend
At last!

Samantha Gunn (9)
St Joseph's RC Primary School, Rossington

My Dream Yacht

My yacht
As blue as a sapphire
On the calm waters
Anchored down
Like a stone on the beach

My yacht
As red as a ruby
On the ocean waves
Being pitched about
Like a simulator at the fair

My yacht
As gold as treasure
On the river banks
Static on the sand
Like a diamond statue

My yacht
As green as an emerald
On the marina's waters
Cruising away
Like a plane in the sky

My yacht
As orange as the sun
Sailing through the black of night
On the River Humber
Like a silver wedding ring

My yacht
As black as jet
In a photograph
In the Boat Trader
Waiting for me to buy it!

Sam Squires (10)
St Joseph's RC Primary School, Rossington

Beautiful Winter

When you see a smiling snowman
Winter has finally arrived
The rosy-red cheeks of the children playing
Lights up the plain white snow

The trees are now like an empty hat stand
And are swaying to the cold wind
Their branches are tipped with glistening snow
And the icicles on the branches make a beautiful tune
As they tinkle together gracefully

Then a robin drifts onto a mulberry bush
Its red breast lighting up the dull sky
It puts his head in his feathers
Its tiny body shivering

Finally the moon
Shining like a new pin rises into the starry night
The Earth is covered with total darkness
Now the snow looks grey while everyone rests

The next day the snow has melted
And the smiling snowman is a pile of sticks
And two gloves lay on the rough ground
For the first time in three months the sun is glowing
Like a flaming torch
Winter has ended.

Jake Bowden (11)
St Joseph's RC Primary School, Rossington

My Father

My father took me into the garden one night,
And we counted the twinkling stars, one by one.
Then, out of the clouds, there came a glowing, white silhouette.
My father told me, that this was the moon.
It looked very beautiful, against the pitch-black sky.

I tried to reach it, but I couldn't,
So I started to cry,
And my tears came down, like falling crystals.
My father said I would never be able to reach it.
I stopped crying immediately, but it wasn't because of this . . .
It was because of something else . . .

A mysterious shape was creepily emerging from the clouds.
It was a bomber plane, from Germany.
My father rushed inside, with me in his arms,
And tried to turn all the lights out,
But it was too late.
Crash! Bang! My father was dead.
I will probably remember this dreadful night,
Of losing my best friend, 'til the day I die . . .

Rebecca Middleton (10)
St Joseph's RC Primary School, Rossington

A Fascinating Dream

Imagine the moon was made of milk chocolate,
Free for anyone to eat,
Or imagine it was a huge white pearl,
For anyone to gaze at its shimmers of white.
Imagine the moon was square, like a cream brick,
Or imagine it was rectangular like a long ruler.

Imagine that the moon was orange,
Or if it was the shape of a pear with the stalk on the top,
What if it was real,
What would that be like?

But what if there were aliens on it that danced on it all night,
And what if there was a mountain full of sticky toffee chocolate,
Bubbling out of the top.
What would that be like?

Imagine if the moon was made of candle wax,
And what if it was made of paper,
Or even if it was made of white rose petals
What would that be like?

Suppose all of that was true, what would that be like?
What if the moon was a fluffy candy stepping stone
Leading you into a fantasy world,
What would that be like?
Oh it would be like a fascinating dream!

Claudia Calzini (10)
St Joseph's RC Primary School, Rossington

Wintertime Is Here

The snow falling from the sky
Making a thick layer of snow
Like a blanket left on the ground.

The Christmas tree in the living room
Standing in the corner like a pole strong and straight
Not even a bend.

The fireplace in the dining room
All covered with tinsel and balls
Wintertime is here, it's here already.

A crash upon the roof, is Santa up there I wonder?
Bells jingling in the wind
As soft as it can sound.

Santa's in our house, I can hear him sipping the milk
It sounds as though he's finished
'Goodbye Santa for another year!'

Naomi Horan (11)
St Joseph's RC Primary School, Rossington

Living Things

Buttercups in the meadow,
Daisies in the field,
Seaweed in the water,
Clouds in the sky.

Girls reading books,
Boys grabbing hooks,
Bulbs growing, raindrops falling,
The sun's come out to set.

Conkers on the ground,
Trees standing up.
The wind is blowing
There is a world of all kinds of things.

Amy Greenaway (9)
St Joseph's RC Primary School, Rossington

At The End Of The Lane

Just on my doorstep and not far away
There's a special place I go.
When the sun is out and high in the sky
Things never make me feel low.
I've taken my friends in the summer break,
They thought it was beautiful too!
We scrambled through plants to get to the view,
A lovely small lake we saw with flowers and butterflies all around,
So colourful and bright and more.
We looked at each other and smiled with a grin,
I was so happy inside,
And knew deep down this was the place if I was sad,
That I would come and hide.

Emily Hall (9)
St Joseph's RC Primary School, Rossington

Our Moon

In the night sky
The moon is seated
Glowing as bright as an angel's halo.

It's as round as a football
Towering in the sky
Looking down into the colourful Earth.

On the dark, dull nights
It lights up the sky
Like a pearl with a heart of fire.

It gleams with brightness
Like a candle in a cupboard of darkness
Lighting up a path to Heaven.

Amy Wilkinson (10)
St Joseph's RC Primary School, Rossington

Anger

I could feel the pressure inside me,
It was building up,
My face was bright red,
It was like fireworks blasting.

My head was about to explode,
My heart pumping,
You could see the faint steam,
My face told a story.

I came to the point,
Where I went *bang!*
My veins were popping,
I shouted as loud as bombs.

I banged the door,
Stamped my feet,
Threw lots of things,
I was like a big shark eating fish.

I charged at the exit door,
My fists were clenched,
I was a volcano,
My stomach turned like a washing machine.

Yousuf Ahmed (10)
St Mary's Catholic Primary School, Bradford

Anger

Kettle whistling like a puff from my head.
Like burning from your throat before you scream.
Smells like fire on a burnt house.
Like a rocket on fire, what a big noise it made
It reminds me of my dad shouting as loud as a gorilla.

Ayesha Ahmed (9)
St Mary's Catholic Primary School, Bradford

Very Angry

Back off!
My anger is growing,
It's like a raging bull seeing red.
A ferocious rhino charging.
It's the enthusiasm of a tiger.
It's the fury of the dragon's flame.
I can't control myself,
It's like a car going out of control.
The anger is like poison,
As angry as a lion.
It's the force of the elements,
As big as a planet.
Back off!
Back off!
I'm warning you.
Back off!
Back off!
The force of a tornado,
The power of a typhoon.

Aiden Halstead (10)
St Mary's Catholic Primary School, Bradford

Anger

It sounds like burning fire
It tastes like burnt toast with
No butter or jam.
It smells like thick black
Smoke.
It looks like a cat hissing.
It feels like hot blood inside of me
It reminds me of scary stuff and when I
Was angry yesterday.

Ashleigh Stronge (9)
St Mary's Catholic Primary School, Bradford

Anger

It sounds like someone snoring,
When you're trying to sleep.
It tastes like a spicy curry,
Burning your tongue as you eat.
It smells like a fire,
Burning down the house.
It looks like the face of a bull,
Chasing down the red cloak,
It feels like you're burning inside
Ready to explode like a rocket into
The sky.
Anger building up,
Reminds me of a shaken pop bottle,
Bubbling over like a volcano,
Sitting, hissing, fizzing.

Aidan Rhodes (9)
St Mary's Catholic Primary School, Bradford

Sadness

It sounds like dogs yapping
All day long, looking for attention.
It tastes like nasty medicine
What a stupid invention!
It smells like mouldy cheese,
God, it makes me heave.
It looks like my mum with a sad face
It's usually my fault every single day.
It's like sitting all alone in the dark
Sitting, listening to not a sound, not a spark.
It's like my parents arguing!
Why do they do it?
I ask myself.

Rochelle Davico (9)
St Mary's Catholic Primary School, Bradford

Anger

I could feel it building up in my guts
I started to screech like elephants
'Get away from me!
I hate you all!
All of you get away!'
My eyes are as red as lava
I feel like I am going to burst
'I hate you!
Get away from me!'
I ran down the stairs
A stampede of horses
I feel like a machine gun, firing bullets
A crocodile snapping at its prey.

'No . . . no . . . no!'

Warren Charles (10)
St Mary's Catholic Primary School, Bradford

Fear

It tastes like your mouth is dry,
Like the taste buds aren't working,
Fear smells like there is nothing there!
. . . Hang on; do any of my senses work?
. . . Oh yeah,
It sounds like the dripping of a tap
In a dark haunted house at night.
It looks like a spider's shadow creeping up the wall in the moonlight,
It's cold and damp like rain on the pavement,
It reminds me of nothing . . .
My mind is empty . . .
Waiting for something to happen.

Paige Uttley (9)
St Mary's Catholic Primary School, Bradford

Lonely

Standing in the doorway,
Feeling so upset,
With everybody staring,
Feeling glum, unhappy, hurt.

So black and dirty,
My clothes filthy and foul,
Untidy, messy,
Not even clothes . . .
Just pieces of material.

Tears in my eyes,
Nobody cares, I am just dirt,
Off the streets,
Feeling heartbroken.

Where can I go?
No place,
No family to go to,
No friends.

I'm so tired and lonely,
Going to break into pieces,
Shattering like hailstones on the floor,
That's why I am so lonely!

Tiger-Lily Crawford (10)
St Mary's Catholic Primary School, Bradford

Anger

Like a whistle on fire that's burnt.
Like burnt toast that's been on fire.
Smells like a roast chicken that is on fire.
Like a pig that's so boring and the haystack that's burning.
Like a hot fire on a summer day.
Like a whistling kettle at my cousin's.

Shamima Rashid (10)
St Mary's Catholic Primary School, Bradford

Anger

It's here!
The part of me that is a monster,
Rampaging through the jungle like an elephant,
Dynamite ready to go off,
The anger couldn't be controlled,
It is like a gorilla in a cage,
A shark,
Tearing apart a small fish,
A raging bull
Knocking down a weak matador,
A hurricane, destroying cities.

It's here!
It's taking control,
It's going to explode,
Get out!
I'm dangerous,
I'm like a hungry golden eagle,
A venomous cobra,
A giant T-rex
Be warned . . .
Bang!
Too late!

Rorie Campbell (10)
St Mary's Catholic Primary School, Bradford

Love

It sounds like a mother comforting her baby,
When it's crying through the night.
It tastes like the juice of a passion fruit,
All sweet and mouth watering.
It smells like a cream cake in a cake shop,
Appetizing and fulfilling.
It looks like the waves going on your feet.
It feels like sitting on a beach in hot weather.
It reminds me of love.

Nadia Keren Hussain (9)
St Mary's Catholic Primary School, Bradford

Anger

I clench my fist,
Pull my hair,
Stamp on the floor like an elephant,
I'm going to blow,
I'm going . . . I'm going . . . I've gone . . . *bang!*
No! No! No!
I throw my shoe at the door.
I run out and screamed *'Argh!'*
My ears are full of steam,
I am burning up like a fireball from the sky,
I explode like a balloon,
I can feel it,
I don't care,
It's starting to hurt,
Don't talk to me I'm trying to calm down,
Go away,
Leave me alone,
I'm going to do something I will regret.

Toni-Louise Mudd (10)
St Mary's Catholic Primary School, Bradford

Happiness

It sounds like enchanted music on a summer's evening,
It tastes like a piece of chocolate melting on my tongue,
It smells like a candy wrapper,
It takes the form of my mum,
It feels like my mum,
It reminds me of my mum.

Matthew Butler (9)
St Mary's Catholic Primary School, Bradford

I Could Feel It!

I could feel it
Burning inside me
Like a stampede
The bigger it got
The more I felt like
Bursting!
Then it hit me
I exploded
Started stomping
Charging like a bull
Screaming and shouting
Bawling and screeching.
It was too much
I ran upstairs
Slammed the door
It was over
Phew!

Rosie Griffin (10)
St Mary's Catholic Primary School, Bradford

Anger

It felt like a hurricane
Sucking up everything in my way
My head was going to pop
Like a paper bag.
A balloon overfilled with air
Going to go *bang!*
My blood was going to burst a vein
I turned red in my face
I stomped upstairs into my room
Jumped onto my bed
Shouted, *'Go away!'*
My anger had calmed down, it was over . . .

Benjamin Dunne (10)
St Mary's Catholic Primary School, Bradford

Anger

As angry as a tiger,
Blood boiling,
Like a lion fighting,
Losing temper - angry, fierce, strong
Feel like a volcano,
Eyes staring fiercely,
Foot stamping, kicking, punching,
Shouting loudly, losing control,
Nagging, hitting,
Fighting like a shark snapping,
I could feel it coming very close,
Go away!
But it would not,
Coming very close . . .
I was scared
Then angry like a volcano,
Shouted but it won't go away.
My blood was boiling.
My eyes were fierce
Everywhere I wanted to fight like a tiger.

Harvir Bassi (10)
St Mary's Catholic Primary School, Bradford

Angry

It was like a firework about to explode
I could feel it inside me.
Slamming doors
Telling people to go away.
It was building up inside
I exploded!
Throwing things
Shouting
I was really cross
Charging
Like a mad bull.

Liam Delaney (10)
St Mary's Catholic Primary School, Bradford

Help

Standing in the doorway
Feeling so sad
So hungry.
Standing with ripped clothes
Everyone laughing.
Feeling so alone.
So black and dirty.
My clothes are all ragged,
A black face,
I am heartbroken.

Tears in my eyes
Nobody helping me
I am hungry,
Untidy face,
Nobody looked after me.
Where can I go?
There was no place for me.

Rahul Sharma (10)
St Mary's Catholic Primary School, Bradford

Desperate

Standing in the doorway
Feeling lonely and sad
Unhappy and upset
So black and dirty
My clothes ripped and torn
Rags, muddy and messy
Tears in my eyes
Nobody cares
Nobody to love
And no friends.

What kind of life is this?

Matthew Pryce (10)
St Mary's Catholic Primary School, Bradford

Lonely

Standing in the doorway
Feeling heartbroken
Nobody cares about me!
Why do people stare?

So black and dirty
My clothes ripped
I wish I could buy some new ones.

Tears in my eyes
Nobody cares anymore
I wish right now I was in a warm house
Where can I go?

No place to go
I wish somebody would help me!
I'm so tired and lonely
Feeling glum!

Please help me!

Siani Simpson (10)
St Mary's Catholic Primary School, Bradford

Dirty

Standing in the doorway
Feeling thirsty and miserable
Sick and very scared.

So black and dirty
My clothes torn and filthy
My hair muddy and greasy.

Tears in my eyes
Nobody cares
I'm disliked and unloved.

Where can I go?
No place, no home
No one loves me anymore
So tired and hungry.

I'm so sick and lonely
Feeling unwanted and ugly
I'm so annoyed and angry
But what can I do if no one loves me?

Christine Wadby (10)
St Mary's Catholic Primary School, Bradford

Alone

Standing in the doorway
Feeling heartbroken
With my clothes ripped
In shreds, feeling miserable.

So black and dirty
My clothes torn to pieces
Does anybody love me?
What will happen?

Tears in my eyes
Nobody cares
Rolling down my face
Feeling sorry for myself.

Where can I go?
No place to live
Feeling tired
And sick.

I'm so tired and lonely
Feeling very hungry
Does anybody care . . .
If I die?

Lee Clayton (10)
St Mary's Catholic Primary School, Bradford

Anger

I could taste it
It was in me
I could feel it
It was thrashing like a shark in the sea
Ready to eat everyone I meet.
A bull with a samurai sword
A bomb ticking
Until I explode . . .
Bang!
I was very angry
I charged into doors like a bull
A falcon catching its prey
I swoop down on it
It's dead
I lose it and charge
Argh!

Nathan Weeks (10)
St Mary's Catholic Primary School, Bradford

Anger

Anger is like the colour yellow
It sounds like splodges
It tastes like food that's gone-off
It smells awful
It feels like cement
It reminds me of a yellow bucket of paint.

Georgia England (8)
St Paul's J&I School, Alverthorpe

Anger

Anger makes me see the colour red like fiery hot flames.
It makes me hear an angry charging bull.
When I'm angry it tastes like lots of onions.
When I'm full of anger it makes me smell burning flames
burning down the house.
It makes me feel like I'm walking on burning coal.
It reminds me of my mum and dad splitting up and getting divorced.

Oliver Richardson (8)
St Paul's J&I School, Alverthorpe

Anger

It sounds like a little girl screaming in the woods, *'Argh!'*
It tastes like pickled onions and spicy chicken with BBQ sauce.
It smells like dry blood.
It makes me feel hard and tough.
It reminds me of when I got lost in Eureka and I could not find
my mum or my dad.

Casey Harris (8)
St Paul's J&I School, Alverthorpe

Anger

Anger is grey like the rough pavement.
It sounds like a loud erupting dangerous volcano.
It tastes like hot, boiling porridge swirling through my mouth.
It smells like horrible burnt toast.
It feels like the pain in my head when I fell.
It reminds me of an exploding volcano.

Joseph Cobbold (8)
St Paul's J&I School, Alverthorpe

Laughter

Laughter is blue like the summer sky.
It sounds like jokes spilling out of our mouths.
It tastes like French fries salted from McDonald's.
It smells like the fresh melon which has just been cut open.
It feels like a fluffy cloud.
It reminds me of splashing water from a waterfall.

Peter Spurr (8)
St Paul's J&I School, Alverthorpe

Sadness

Sadness is like the colour red
Because when you cry your eyes go red.
Sadness sometimes makes your mouth taste dry.
It feels like a big pain in your heart inside and out.
Sadness reminds me of a wet weekend.
Sadness sounds like thunder billowing in my head.

Jessica Walker (9)
St Paul's J&I School, Alverthorpe

Fear

Fear is black like the fear of the dark.
It sounds like someone screaming in horror.
It tastes like bitter spices.
It smells like someone dying.
It feels like gunk.
It reminds me of a burning fire.

Jonathan Cotterill (8)
St Paul's J&I School, Alverthorpe

Fear

Fear is grey smoke burning from a building.
Fear sounds like the screaming of frightened children.
Fear tastes like spicy curry.
Fear smells like smoke burning from a building on fire.
Fear feels like my head is going to pop off at any moment.
Fear reminds me of getting hurt and having nobody to help me.

Laura Wilkes (8)
St Paul's J&I School, Alverthorpe

Sadness

Sadness is like the colour navy.
It sounds like the crying of a baby.
And it tastes of hot chilli.
Sadness smells like vinegar.
It feels like a spiky conker.
It reminds me of fire.

Amy Williams (9)
St Paul's J&I School, Alverthorpe

Happiness

Happiness is like a yellow lemon.
It tastes sweet, sour and juicy.
Happiness sounds of laughter at a wedding or a party.
It also smells like honey.
It feels lumpy and soft.
It reminds me of lemon juice.

Kimberley Bateman (8)
St Paul's J&I School, Alverthorpe

Happiness

Happiness is the reddest rose growing in my garden.
Happiness sounds like loud laughter echoing in my room.
Happiness is like strawberries and cream in a bowl, waiting
to be eaten.
Happiness is like the cheesy smell of pizza going through
every room of my house.
Happiness is like my furry teddy I take to bed every night.
Happiness is like my smelly rose growing in my window.

Keeley Oxley (8)
St Paul's J&I School, Alverthorpe

Fear

Fear is like my heart beating.
It tastes like cold air.
Smells fresh.
Feels creepy.
Reminds me of the time I opened a spooky closet.

Danny Armstrong (8)
St Paul's J&I School, Alverthorpe

Love

Sounds like happy laughter.
Tastes like the most delicious curry in my life.
It feels like my heart is on fire.
It smells like the scent of a flower.

Louis Jackson (8)
St Paul's J&I School, Alverthorpe

Happiness

Happiness is yellow like the golden sun.
It sounds like the birds singing in the trees.
It tastes like sweet candyfloss at the fair.
It smells like fresh flowers in the park.
It feels like a rabbit in some hay.
It reminds me of when I went to one of my friend's parties.

Rebecca Sharkey (8)
St Paul's J&I School, Alverthorpe

Anger

Anger is red like a booming fire.
It sounds like a bloodthirsty beast.
It tastes like dripping blood.
It smells like a lonely swamp.
It feels like a huge vampire.
It reminds me of a spooky forest.

Euan Toms (8)
St Paul's J&I School, Alverthorpe

Love

Love is red like a beautiful rose.
It sounds like joyful music at a party.
It tastes like sweet wine at a wedding.
It smells like melted chocolate on top of ice cream.
It feels like soft, silky clothes.
It reminds me of happy children playing outside.

Nicole Nicholson (8)
St Paul's J&I School, Alverthorpe

White As A Ghost

Fear is white as a ghost,
Getting darker with the dark,
Once you see it you freeze,
It's quiet and silent,
It tastes of egg,
It smells of tea,
It feels like thin air,
It makes me think of when I saw the Tooth Fairy
But it looked like a ghost.

Macauley Pritchard (8)
St Paul's J&I School, Alverthorpe

Anger

Anger is like the colour red.
It sounds like shouting.
It tastes like hot curry.
It smells like garlic bread.
It feels like I am burning in an oven.

Jake Stainthorpe (8)
St Paul's J&I School, Alverthorpe

Joy

Joy is blue like the fantastic summer sky.
It sounds like a beautiful bird singing wonderfully.
It tastes like a lovely juicy melon.
It smells like a fresh crunchy apple just bitten into.
It feels like the fluffy fur of a lamb.
It reminds me of the footballer Danny Pugh.

Sam Malley (8)
St Paul's J&I School, Alverthorpe

Hate

Hate is red like blood and black like oil.
It sounds like scary, horror, creepy noises.
It tastes like tomato and I hate the smell of cheese.
It feels like burning fire.
It reminds me of burnt sausages.

Liam Smith (8)
St Paul's J&I School, Alverthorpe

Love

Love is red like a sweet rose.
It sounds like laughter.
It tastes like a juicy melon.
It smells like flowers.
It feels like people having a party.
It reminds me of Christmas.

Ellie Arnold (8)
St Paul's J&I School, Alverthorpe

Sadness

Sadness is like the colour red.
It sounds like animals choking.
It tastes like a tomato.
It smells like blood.
It feels runny.
It reminds me of when my dad died.

Shane Lindop (8)
St Paul's J&I School, Alverthorpe

Hate

It sounds like harsh, spooky nonsense.
It tastes of tomato.
It smells like oil.
It feels like a hot fire.
It reminds me of the time I was thrown over a bush.
Hate is like a cat and red like blood.

Joseph Wilson (8)
St Paul's J&I School, Alverthorpe

Love

Love is like the colour red.
It sounds like drumming.
It tastes like a juicy strawberry.
It smells like a rose.
It feels like soft fur on a puppy.
It reminds me of my baby cousin.

Megan Pickles (9)
St Paul's J&I School, Alverthorpe

Love

Love is red like the heart.
It sounds like the beating of a drum.
It tastes like strawberries.
It smells like chocolate in the air.
It feels like I am in my snugly warm bed.
It reminds me of my little brother.

Charlotte Stones (8)
St Paul's J&I School, Alverthorpe

Sadness

Sadness is black like a tear dripping off a face.
It sounds like a boat drifting far away.
It tastes like a cold, soft pizza.
It smells like cooked vegetables.
It feels like a cold winter's day.
It reminds me of when I think of my grandad.

Chloe Smith (8)
St Paul's J&I School, Alverthorpe

Anger

Anger is red.
It sounds like shouting.
It tastes like a spicy curry.
It smells like gas.
It feels like you're on fire.
It reminds me of when I burnt my finger.

Max Stokes (8)
St Paul's J&I School, Alverthorpe

Happiness

Happiness is yellow like the bright yellow sun.
It sounds like a cat miaowing.
It tastes like strawberry ice cream.
It smells like candyfloss at a fair.
It feels like I'm in a bed of flowers.
It reminds me of flowers in a field.

Joanne Cotton (8)
St Paul's J&I School, Alverthorpe

Guess What?

Children screaming,
Whistles blowing,
Balls flying.
Leaves dancing,
Trees waving,
Streams flowing.
Teachers shouting,
Girls skipping,
Boys playing.
Sun shining,
People laughing.
What a nice place to be.
Guess what?

School playground.

Georgia Shepheard (9)
Sacred Heart Primary School

Guess What?

It is a warm place,
So very comforting,
Happiness and sadness,
Have treasured it for life.
A place where I am loved.
I feel like I am cared for,
Because I know I am,
So very much!
I have been with it nearly all my life.
I would hate to leave,
I would be terrified,
This warm, loving, caring place is
My house and it is my home!

Erin Crotty (9)
Sacred Heart Primary School

Ties

Yesterday my mum told me to get a new tie,
So I decided to go down to M&S
When I got to M&S,
There were so many ties I ended up in a mess,
There were:
Blue ties
Red ties
Spotty blue and red ties
Green ties
Pink ties
Smelly pink and green ties
Black ties
White ties
Stripy black and white ties
Orange ties
Yellow ties
Light-up orange bow ties
In the end there were so many ties,
I couldn't choose a single one!
So my mum came in and picked me one.

Callum Doherty (9)
Sacred Heart Primary School

Pete The Pirate

Pete the pirate,
King of the seven seas,
As he watches the Lego brick seas,
Shining in the evening sun.
Dressed in golden rags,
In a cardboard crows nest,
Cutlass shining, blood at its tip
He gazes north, 'Pirates' Pete shouted
'We have company' but being played with
I'm just a little doll man!

Benedict Labbett (9)
Sacred Heart Primary School

Ten Things Found In Disgusting Diane's Pocket

Ten things found in disgusting Diane's pocket . . .
A slimy, slippery slug,
A mouldy handful of mud,
A horrible, dead wasp,
A three-day-old egg omelette,
A squished worm,
A potful of three-week honey,
A trayful of maggot pie,
A hairy lollipop,
A piece of horrible, mouldy, cement-flavoured bubblegum
And a piece of snotty tissue.

Olivia Stainton (9)
Sacred Heart Primary School

Underwear

U is for uncomfortable, light and itchy.
N is for naughty, the elastic snaps on me.
D is for dirty, muddy and dark.
E is for embarrassing, pretty and pink.
R is for ragged, rips and tears.
W is for weird, unusually strange.
E is for enormous, baggy and smelly.
A is for absolutely tiny. Thin but small.
R is for ruched, gathered and scrunched.

Big ones, small ones, polka dots, green ones,
Black ones and lots more too.
That spells underwear!

Emma Williams (9)
Sacred Heart Primary School

Ten Things Found in Naughty Nick's Pocket

A strong slingshot,
A smelly stinkbug,
A sticky stick of bubblegum,
A scary spider,
A terrible textbook,
A petrifying pencil,
A fantastic fake scar,
A peculiar penknife,
A spine tingling storybook,
A radioactive remote control car.

Archie Miller (9)
Sacred Heart Primary School

Autumn Leaves

A is for autumn, a time when leaves are gold,
U is for undergrowth, where hedgehogs hide from cold.
T is for trees - they are all going bare,
U is for underfoot, leaves are everywhere!
M is for mist, clearing at dawn,
N is for nuts, buried in the lawn.

L is for leaves, floating to the ground,
E is for each one, swirling around.
A is for apples, in the harvest crop.
V is for veg, from the garden not the shop.
E is for everywhere, leaves fall, it's a pain.
S is for seasons, it's autumn again!

Matthew Procter (9)
Sacred Heart Primary School

One Varied Day

Leaves leap from trees running from the evil tree master,
The sun fights against the clouds desperate to shine first,
The trees dance in the wind swaying from side to side,
Rain throws itself from the clouds to the ground.

Snow flutters in the wind like hair,
The stars twinkled in the sky like startled eyes,
The rain drops from the sky like tears,
The hot summer sun beats down on the waiting grass.

The moon winks a lazy eye at the sun as it goes to bed,
The grass grows as the rain beats down on it,
The petals fly from the flower on to the soft flattened grass,
The sun climbs up to the sky ready to start the day.

Morag Gillon (10)
Sacred Heart Primary School

My Best Friends

My best friends are the best of friends,
The best of friends they are!
One of them can roll their tongue,
One of them can wiggle their ears,
One of them is good at sport,
One of them is into the army,
One of them sometimes goes barmy.
One of them is good at rugby.
One of them is good at cycling.
One of them is a jazzy groover.
One of them is a mental clown.
One of them is still quite young.
One of them is a greedy guts.
The best of friends they
Are!

Oliver Button (9)
Sacred Heart Primary School

The Blitz

Fire crawls across London town,
Reaching to claim lives by licking anything in its sight.

The planes swooped in, cutting the air,
On their way to drop their bombs
That will explode like fireworks on London town.

The bombs loomed like giants' feet
Destroying anything in its sight.

The darkness swallowed everything that moved,
So that you could hear the screams of dying people.

The trains hurtled out of their stations,
Puffing out big clouds of black smoke,
Racing to get away from Hitler's bombs.

Sirens scream in every direction
Warning that there would be another raid on its way once again.

Smoke jumped up as high as it could
To get away from the chaotic events down below.

Houses lay demolished by the crazy bombs
Of the madman *Adolf Hitler!*

Matthew Thompson (11) & James Garside (10)
Sacred Heart Primary School

I Know Someone

I know someone I can trust to keep me calm,
I know someone who is kind and will play with me,
I know someone who is friendly towards everyone,
I know someone who is hardworking and tries their best always.

Niamh Walker (9)
Sacred Heart Primary School

Chocolate

My mum gave me fifty pence
I wonder what I'll get
So I went to the sweet shop and I saw . . .
A curled liquorish
A juicy lip
A milk bottle
Made me think
Now Cadbury's chocolate
Sunny Delight
Gummy pizza
All shone in the light
And
Mini marshmallows
Gummy teeth
Sherbet sticks
Mmm . . .
Gobstoppers
Black Jack
White mice
All scrummy for me
I paused for a moment
And the man said to me
'Look after the shop for a while!'
Then an idea just popped up
I got a bag and filled up
I ran back home showed my mum . . .
'You've got a lot for fifty-one pence!'

James Sutherland (9)
Sacred Heart Primary School

My Peace In The Jungle

My perfect peace is . . .

In a tropical jungle climbing up trees to my tree house.

I can smell the scent of the bananas, and the lovely smell of cocoa beans, the scent of the fresh air and the waterfall drifting up my nose.

I can hear the bellows of the tigers roaring, and the *splish, splash, splosh* of the waterfall.

The elephants trumpeting like boat horns and the parrots squawking as they fly over the jungle.

I can taste juicy pineapples, sweet coconut milk and water trickling down my throat.

I can see my tree house, peeking out from behind the trees.
Monkeys swing around on vines as snakes crawl across the wet floor of the jungle.

Annabelle Jarvis & Chiara Davies (10)
Sacred Heart Primary School

Ten Things I Lost In My Coat Pocket And I Don't Want Back!

My mouldy apple,
My dead snail,
My mouldy slug,
My chopped off finger,
My fake foot,
My skinned banana,
My skeletoid mouse,
My fake eyeball
My squished oranges
My rotting shoe.

Joe Sewell (9)
Sacred Heart Primary School

Seasons

The sun stars washing away the snow.
Lambs start celebrating a new year.
Showers fall with joy from somewhere up above.
Plants yawn out of a deep sleep.

Mother sun smiles brightly down on her nine children
Streams gently whisper on their journey to the rivers.
Waves race each other to the beach.
Bees work busily throughout the day.

Leaves jump excitedly away from their tree father.
Hard conkers fight with one and other.
Icy winds zoom across the fields leaving the grass shivering.
The cackle of the bonfires chattering into the night.

Evil frost hardens the soft ground
Snowflakes fall elegantly down to the earth
Stars dance brightly in the dark night sky
Snowmen cheer up the dismal gardens.

Matthew Wilson (10)
Sacred Heart Primary School

Underwear

Underwear with stripes and spots,
Underwear with polka dots,
Some are black ones,
Some are white ones,
Some are baggy and some are tight ones.
Some must have elastic,
And some are just fantastic,
Some are wacky,
And some are just tacky!

Christina Graham (9)
Sacred Heart Primary School

Take Me To The New Day

The night tells day when to wake up in the morning
In a soft, calling voice that coos,
The moon remembers all that has ever happened,
She is wise and very gentle,
The mountain knows everyone who has walked on him
And shows them his lovely daughters,
The streams bubble over rocks, dancing, talking, laughing,
Climbing on their father the mountain.

The sea listens to the message of the clouds,
The tide shows the sea how to lap at the shore
In an elegant, swishing way of beauty,
The sun sings the word of the stars in the sky,
The hills roll about in the valleys below.

The earth turns, turns softly, turns sweetly, so very majestically,
The stars shine brightly and laugh full of joy,
Nature's own beauty will always surround us,
So, dawn, take me to the bright new day!

Hannah Kearns (10)
Sacred Heart Primary School

Bizarre Happenings

One fine night in the middle of the day,
All of England was found in Pompeii.

With trees climbing cats,
And rabbits chasing dogs.

With houses in people,
And shops in treacle.

With pupils in charge of teachers,
And time in charge of lunch.

All the world was going tipsy,
Just in time for brunch.

Ruth Doherty (10)
Sacred Heart Primary School

A New Day

It is morning.
The sun rises high into the sky smiling happily.
The clouds whisper gently to each other
As the birds soar into the air.
A squirrel runs up the side of a willow,
Making it giggle as it tickles its bark.
The old oak stretches out its long branches
For the birds to perch on.

It is midday.
A dark cloud rumbles in the distance, ready to battle the sun.
The first drops of rain fall heavily on to the ground.
The little pink worms peek up through the soil as not to drown.
The ducks laugh at each other in the pond,
Pecking at the bread left over from last night.

It is evening.
The dark clouds have passed away.
The sun has said farewell and disappeared beyond the horizon.
The moon has come to tell the stars a story
As they fall asleep in the clear night sky.
Everything is silent apart from the buzzing of the small midges.
And so the moon smiles and gives a deep sigh
As she too falls asleep in the dark sky.

Jessica Allan (10)
Sacred Heart Primary School

World War II

The fire crawls across London streets,
Twisting, turning to catch its prey.

The smell of smoke lingers in the air,
Making a thick and dense atmosphere
Wherever we are hiding.

Buildings are screaming as they melt into nothing.

The planes fly over London randomly dropping bombs.

Frances Layfield (10)
Sacred Heart Primary School

The Seasons

I love springtime,
When all the lambs are born,
The days get longer,
You smell the smell of your lawn.

I love summertime,
When you play in your paddling pool,
The grass is green,
And the shade is cool.

I love autumn time,
When all the leaves are gold and red,
The days get shorter,
So you have more time in bed.

I love wintertime,
When the snow gently falls,
You get out your sledge,
And you can't hear other's calls.

I love all seasons!

Natasha Verspyck (10)
Sacred Heart Primary School

A Poem Of Nature

Night it reminds me of yesterday,
The sun listens to the message of the clouds,
The moon tells all the stars a story as they slowly drift asleep.
The mountain remembers every blessed foot walked upon it.

The storm brings fear and black skies,
The sun teaches us how bright it can be,
The sky brings happiness and joy.

The sea performs a gentle dance while flowing,
The stone sighs as it dreams a dream.
Night brings sleep and rest as it smiles and shines in the night sky.

Biagio Ruggiero (11)
Sacred Heart Primary School

Death Is Here

Sirens scream in every direction; warning
Of the deadly gas.
Suffocating anything that stands in its way,
Bringing it to death.
Gas whistles through the air,
Emerging from the silently falling buildings.

Smoke weeps from houses and buildings,
Fire crawls across London town.
Burning everything in its sight
Ear-piercing screams from every house,
Hoping to be heard,
Wanting to be found.

Zoe Jones (10)
Sacred Heart Primary School

Footie Madness!

Coloured faces everywhere
That smell of fast food in the air.

The buzzing of excitement
And nervousness as well
'Oh my God what's that awful smell?'
'It's just my socks,' says Dad.

Players striking, keepers diving,
Forwards celebrating when they score
Making people want some more.

When half-time comes round players leave
The pitch then comes the entertainment.

Players come back on the pitch it's obvious
There's been a switch.

'Look, they're on,' says Dad
The balls are flying the keepers going mad.

The game comes to an end, that was a decent spend.

Gavin Hirst (10)
Wellhouse J&I School

The Sea

The sea is a wonderful place and
You never know what might be lurking deep
Down in the sea.

What a beautiful sight to see.
There's all sorts of different plants
Like blue ones, yellow ones
Red, purple and pink.

I bet with such a nice sight
You would not even blink.

In the sea there are sounds all around.
Like the waves going gently across the water.
But if it's a bad day and very stormy the
Waves are crashing, bashing
Like a bomb has just dropped.

There's other sounds in the sea
Like the boats, rain and the gentle swaying of the plants.

Fish . . . there's lots of fish in the sea
Like whales, rainbow fish, starfish
But
Beware of the sharks -
Hammerhead sharks, man-eating sharks
And tiger sharks.

Well that's all I have to say about
The sea
Enjoy but beware!

Benjamin Franklin (9)
Wellhouse J&I School

Cars: Modifying Mayhem

The police
Take your money
As you go in.

All you can hear
Is music,
Talking and shouting.

Later on
There's revving
As people start to leave.

The air
Fills with
The smell of burning rubber.

You can see
People gathering
And looking at
The beautiful bodywork of the cars.

In the distance
There are magazine crews
From all over the country.

At about half-past ten
Just about everyone's drunk
And the fighting starts.

And a boy in the crowd says
'Can we go home now?
I don't want to get caught
In the fight!'

Josh Ruddiman (10)
Wellhouse J&I School

Football

The whistle has gone, the ball is kicked,
Players running up and down,
The smell of the hot dogs
Sizzling, the burgers being eaten.
Football!

The devastation, the excitement,
There's no hope, but wait,
One back for Town.
Two-one to Lincoln,
Football!

The fans so excited, the Mexican wave,
The chants, another one back,
We could win couldn't we?
Football!

The whistle was blown,
The crowd ran on the pitch,
We're in the final,
Now that's
Football!

Bradley Butler (10)
Wellhouse J&I School

Football Tournament

Football tournament always as fun as
The funniest thing in the world.

With lines all around the pitch,
With dots the size of hailstones,
The grass is as green as an emerald,
With black spots all over,
With the smell of hot dogs sizzling,
Burgers being devoured.

Ben Hinchliffe (9)
Wellhouse J&I School

Christmas Day

It's Christmas Day
Hurray, hurray
I open all my presents
It really is so pleasant.

I saw my massive Christmas tree
It is the best tree ever you see,
I look out my window to see
My garden is an icy sea,
I saw my brother had made a snowman
Even though he had a great tan.

I heard all the Christmas bells
And the stories my dad tells,
I was watching the Bradford Bulls
Then I heard the Christmas carols,
It was getting to midday
And then it was time to play,
My brother started kicking
Then I could smell the chicken.

James Hardy (8)
Wellhouse J&I School

School Poetry

You write, add, play, do ICT and sing it's very tiring most of the time.
You always see teachers and children.

People shout in the playground, they sing in the hall
And it smells like polish.

Out in the playground some people fight
And some people have no friends and they are like me.

Rosie Lang (9)
Wellhouse J&I School

When I'm Out On The Wreck

When I'm on the wreck,
I can hear,
Swings creaking,
See-saw squeaking,
Chattering,
Nattering,
Footballs slapping against the wall!

When I'm out on school playgrounds,
I can hear all the sounds,
And I'm out with all my mates,
Oh yer also my little mates!

When I'm out at the shop,
I drop all my pop,
Then my mates laugh at me,
The shopkeeper sees me!

When I'm out at the wreck,
I can hear,
Swings creaking,
See-saws squeaking,
Chattering,
Nattering,
Footballs slapping against the wall!
That's all!

Dannii-Louise Kelly (9)
Wellhouse J&I School

Football

White markings round the side of the football pitch.
Green grass with sparkling studs sticking in the paces.
Goal posts with mud stuck to the side and rust all over them.
Blue tops, white shorts, white socks running all over the place.
The crowd screaming and cheering you on and shouting score.

Jack Freeth (9)
Wellhouse J&I School

Christmas Time

It's Christmas Day
And we're going to the bay.
And we're going to go there the right way.
Right we're here, but where's Kay?
She's gone away
But I told her to stay.

At home again
I went outside to build a snowman.
When I got there, there was a snowman.
I knew this was Kay because she was here
But no it wasn't, it was the cat next door
And our neighbour called Dave
With his cat called Wayne.
I went in to find Kay
I could smell the turkey and
The smell of perfume, it smelt gorgeous.

Ilona Baines (10)
Wellhouse J&I School

Air Show

Jet engines as loud as monsters,
People walking as slow as tortoises,
As far as I can see cars are like sea.

People speaking as Chatterbox Charley
Crowds clapping, people cheering.

People jumping with excitement
Flags waving like at a football pitch.
What is this? A plane sparkling, sizzling and bang.
Boom!

Daniel Bagga (9)
Wellhouse J&I School

Visiting Grandma's

Visiting Grandma's is a lovely place to visit.
She always cares like gold for you once or twice.
She loves to clean but always wants to know your secrets.
Once or twice she cooks meat or vegetables.
Reads the magazine of course.
You always find the smells - comforting chips, sweets and meat.
And my grandma smells of perfume a lot of the time.
I think the sounds are comforting with television, oven and
feet stamping.
The rustling of papers and cupboard doors slamming.
The sights are astounding with trains passing and my
grandma's flowers in the garden.

Nathaniel Carter (9)
Wellhouse J&I School

Autumn

One very cold night
I stood by the warm blazing fire
Feeling the hot air and sparks flying around.

The fog surrounding tight,
Like it was wrapping around me as a snake.
All I could see was the big multicoloured flames beaming at me.

There's a loud constant rustling all around,
It's the trees and bags getting blown on the ground.
The leaves of the golden trees lay still, forgotten, undisturbed.

Alice Deans (10)
Wellhouse J&I School

Hallowe'en Night

The monsters stroll along the street very late at night,
'Happy Hallowe'en' they say over and over again,
Mystic knights, scary frights, ghouls and ghosts at last,
Trick or treat here they come,
Closer and closer and closer still,
They're here at last,
Screams and scares all over the place.

Knock, knock, knocking on the door,
You'd better hide quick,
They're coming for ya.

The screams are getting higher, the knocks are getting louder,
Everywhere you look there are monsters.

Lanterns, light and scary knights.

Jack Humphreys (10)
Wellhouse J&I School

A Boy At School

I know a boy at school who talks back at the teacher,
He can say the alphabet backwards,
He plays football like a bull terrier.
He also runs like a cheetah,
He never stops unless he is in school,
If he pours milk in his eyes it will sting but it will come
out of his mouth.

Kurtis Newsome Knight (9)
Wellhouse J&I School

Weather

Snow crackling beneath my feet.
I'm all wrapped up,
But I can't feel any heat.
All my friends built a snowman,
They all threw snowballs as we ran.

Now sun is something everyone loves
Because you don't have to wear your old sweaty gloves.
But when it comes to night
Everything is in sight.

Rain can be fun when you're jumping in puddles
Laughing at your mums and dads standing in huddles.

Wind is useful when flying kites
But when it's very strong
It's not a pretty sight.

In the morning when it's misty and foggy
Everything damp and soggy.

As I watch the frost settle
And the sun comes out
The whole world turns into the steam from a kettle.

Weather, weather everywhere has weather
Wind makes you feel as light as a feather
Rain makes you feel damp
Sun is like a giant lamp.

Laura Jolly (10)
Wellhouse J&I School

A Cold Winter's Night

On a cold winter's night I'm sat by the fire,
I was soaking wet but now I'm getting drier.

I'm very tired and the wind keeps blowing,
I'm drinking hot chocolate and the snow is falling.
There's people shouting in the streets.

The snow's crackling, there's children playing,
Building snowmen and the trees are swaying.

I can smell my hot chocolate and smoke from the fire,
I'm falling asleep I'm getting tireder
And tireder and tireder . . .

Hannah Gee (10)
Wellhouse J&I School

Football

At a football match.
You can smell the sweaty T-shirt.
You can smell the delicious hot dogs.
And singing and shouting like a barmy man
Being drunk. Keepers diving
If they did not dive they would let the goal in.

Football, football
If you score the goal when you celebrate
Don't show your butt.
The game is over and the team celebrate
Until you leave the stadium gates.

Joe Frost (9)
Wellhouse J&I School